Leatherhead Food RA

your partner for today's solutions
and tomorrow's opportunities

FOOD ALLERGY
ISSUES
FOR THE
FOOD INDUSTRY

Edited by
Professor M. Lessof

Published by the
British Food Manufacturing Industries Research Association
Randalls Road, Leatherhead, Surrey KT22 7RY, England

First Edition 1997
ISBN No: 0 905 748 21 2

© 1997 Leatherhead Food RA

PREFACE

When good, wholesome foods are manufactured and marketed under well-controlled conditions, they can still pose a threat to unfortunate individuals who are allergic to one of the ingredients. A problem that was almost unknown - or at least unrecognised - twenty years ago is now a matter of concern not only to allergy sufferers but also to industry and to the regulatory authorities. The increasingly publicised dangers of food allergy and the ever-changing regulatory requirements for food labelling are a source of confusion to many of those who work in the food industry. This book is therefore designed to review the background to the problems that have developed. It will consider - from the industrialist's viewpoint - the pitfalls that may arise when manufactured foods are sold that contain varying or undeclared ingredients of a type that can cause problems for unduly sensitive people.

As yet, there has been no single source to which the manufacturer or the retailer or restaurateur could refer for information about these new developments. This book fills this gap by reviewing the nature of food intolerance, the efforts which have been made to protect members of the public who may be at risk, and the potential problems that could arise when reactions occur.

That there has been an increase in serious and life-threatening reactions to food there can be little doubt. People with a family history of hay fever, asthma, eczema or other allergic disorders are most at risk, but the genetic make-up of the individual cannot be the whole explanation. Nor can an increased awareness or better diagnostic methods, since some of the reactions - for example to peanut - are often so severe and immediate that they can hardly have remained unrecognised in the past. Attention has therefore focused on recent changes in food composition and dietary habits, and on the increased consumption of processed ("ready") foods with a wider range of ingredients and more potentially "hidden" minor components. There has also been much interest in the way in which these changes may affect atopic (i.e. allergic) people, including the very young, who are particularly liable to develop allergies and may, with the decline in breast feeding, encounter a much wider range of foods at a very early age.

Current food labelling requirements present a particular problem to the manufacturer who may have to vary the ingredients of a product with little or no warning and to cope with national and international differences in manufacturing procedures and legislation. When, from time to time, the Codex Alimentarius regulatory requirements are debated and revised, manufacturers of pre-packaged foods may be forgiven for their doubts about both the practicality and the effectiveness of the increasingly complex regulations that are imposed upon them.

When the major ingredients of a product are indicated on the product label, this can provide useful nutritional information but cannot satisfy the need of the food-allergic shopper who may have a reaction to minor, unlabelled ingredients that are present in trace amounts or may even have been carried over from previous products on the same production line. In such circumstances, the potential liability of the manufacturer and the marketer may seem daunting, especially to the international lawyer. In practice, the lawyers' warnings have often been ignored, for example in the provision of "user-friendly" lists of proprietary foods that are free from ingredients such as cows' milk or egg. Those in the food industry who contribute to or distribute lists of this kind have to decide whether the risks to which the lawyers draw attention are theoretical or real and whether their wish to provide a popular service should outweigh those risks. The increased use of "free-from" lists in European countries and in South Africa suggests that many have so decided, but as Neville Craddock has indicated, there can be only a very limited role, if any, for "free-from" lists in respect of life-threatening allergens such as peanut. That warning may be of particular relevance to multi-national companies whose products vary in composition in different manufacturing plants. The peanut is not the only allergen to consider, since other nuts can also be dangerous. Much more problematic, however, is the question of whether this warning should be extended to other products, since there have also been very rare instances of fatal or near-fatal reaction to the very foods about which the food-allergic shopper most often needs help, such as cows' milk or egg. Parents of children with such allergies need and crave advice (with whatever reservations it may be given) and, except for the most severely allergic children, the popularity of 'free-from' lists speaks for itself. Whether provided through supermarkets, dieticians or central databanks, the adoption of such lists in an increasing number of countries suggests that they are greatly valued and that they are here to stay.

The catering industry faces a different set of problems. There have been a number of cases in which diners who have a known food allergy have unwittingly been exposed to trace amounts of a food to which they react. There is a need for staff to be trained about the care to be taken before answering customer queries about potentially dangerous food components, and there is a need for a greater awareness among caterers and restaurateurs of the nature of the problems faced. Here, too, this book can serve a useful purpose.

Maurice Lessof
October 1997

CONTENTS

CONTRIBUTORS

Professor Maurice Lessof
8 John Spencer Square, London N1 2LZ

Neville Craddock
Nestlé UK Ltd, St George's House, Croydon CR9 1NR

Dr Steve L Taylor and Dr Susan L Hefle
University of Nebraska, Food Allergy & Resource Program
Food Processing Center, Lincoln NE 68583-0919 USA

Dr Jonathan O'B Hourihane
Lecturer in Immunobiology
Institute of Child Health
Great Ormond Street Hospital
London WC1N 3EH

Jane Smith
Leatherhead Food Research Association, Randalls Road
Leatherhead, Surrey KT22 7RY

Bernard O'Connor
O'Connor and Company, European Lawyers
Rue de Spa 30, B-1000 Brussels, Belgium

AN OVERVIEW OF FOOD ALLERGY

Maurice Lessof

BACKGROUND

The concept of food allergy is not new. Among the population at large, there are many who have never consulted a doctor but who avoid shellfish because it gives them a rash, red wine because it provokes their asthma, or spices or condiments such as mustard because they make their lips swell or their throat tingle. The scientific background to these reactions to food has, however, emerged slowly, and it is only relatively recently that food allergy has been studied seriously and that allergy has been recognised as a type of immune response that can sometimes do more harm than good. Allergic reactions are known to be largely protective against childhood infections, which are particularly likely to occur in large families or in poor hygienic conditions. When, however, there is less infection to cope with, allergic reactions often appear, perversely, to cause damage by producing exaggerated reactions to harmless dust mites, pollens or food.[1]

Allergy to food is a special case in point. Since food is essential to life, and food allergy involves unpleasant reactions to it, this is a clear example of immunity gone wrong. Allergy is not, however, the only mechanism that interferes with the proper digestion and absorption of nutrients and should not be confused with other varieties of food intolerance, which are sometimes quite mild and may need different management. When this is not recognised, patients with mild food intolerance may be given unnecessarily restricted diets in the mistaken belief that they have a severe allergy. The medical profession has been slow to respond to this challenge, and there are few scientifically based clinics that are equipped to deal with problems of this kind.

The recognition of food allergy is not without its difficulties. There are - and always have been - complex emotions surrounding food, and 'allergic' explanations are frequently offered to provide an acceptable, 'respectable' explanation for obesity, lethargy, depression, or aversions to food that have nothing to do with allergy. Food fads are particularly common in the infant, the adolescent, and those under stress. A parent who is intent on feeding a child may come up against the the infant's first expression of its own will, either accepting or rejecting particular foods which it may come to regard as tokens of comfort or offence. In later life, the emotions associated with food may be equally fraught. Young women in western society have well-developed concepts of body image, and dietary restrictions and bulimic binges have become extremely common among them. Food fads are also common among psychiatric patients, especially in patients who have an obsessional neurosis. Current nostrums concerning food or food allergy as causes of ill health have also encouraged some curiously introspective attitudes, which have been reflected in a wide range of eating disorders. A few vulnerable people, impressed by the belief that they have a 'total allergy', have been led to reject a widening range of foods and have even sequestered themselves in isolated bungalows or caravans. In one such case, there was so much local and media excitement that local schools were persuaded to join in fund-raising efforts to provide the cost of special accommodation for the patient.

The diagnosis of food allergy by parents of small children has also been a matter for concern because, while true in some cases, it can be very misguided in others. Food allergy has become almost a cult, and parents have sometimes given their children obsessional, inappropriate and inadequate diets, based on a vaguely conceived food allergy diagnosis. There have also been cases in which symptoms have been deliberately fabricated in the so-called Münchausen's disease by proxy (named after the outrageous Baron Münchausen of the children's tales). Some of these children have been subjected to highly restrictive régimes in what is now recognised as a form of child abuse.

DEFINITIONS

Food intolerance is the term used for any kind of reproducible adverse reaction to a specific food or food ingredient, provided that it is not psychologically based.[2] 'Adverse reactions to food' is an alternative term which is sometimes favoured. Psychological influences are important but are relatively easy to distinguish. They usually lead to a strong aversion to a food, which the individual believes is bound to provoke symptoms. When the food is given in a disguised form, which cannot be recognised by the person who is being tested, its harmlessness is quickly established.

Food allergy is one particular form of food intolerance, which involves the immune system, but there are other causes of unpleasant reactions to food (see Table 1.I). An important feature of food intolerance is that the reaction is reproducible on more than one occasion, in contrast to the reactions to contaminated, decayed, or infected food, which occur on a single occasion only, sometimes as part of an outbreak that affects a number of people simultaneously.

TABLE 1.I
Adverse reactions to food
(Alternative names: food intolerance or food sensitivity)

	Characteristics	Mechanism
Food allergy	Usually quick - e.g. in skin, lungs, gut	An immune reaction
Food toxicity	Often stomach and bowel effects	Direct toxic damage
Drug effects	E.g. caffeine or caffeine withdrawal: effects are dose-related	Acts on enzymes, cell receptors, etc.
Enzyme deficiency	E.g. failure to digest lactose, alcohol	Faulty metabolism
Malabsorption	E.g. in fatty diarrhoea or other types of unabsorbed food residues	Fermentation in colon

THE IMMUNE SYSTEM AND ALLERGY

When the immune system comes in contact with outside agents, the ability to distinguish between foreign substances and 'self' is key. Foreign substances provoke a defensive reaction, but proteins that are 'recognised' as self (or as harmless) induce a state of tolerance, which then persists. The mechanisms of tolerance are very specific and apply to the body's own tissues but also to individual foods. Once recognised, each individual food is normally tolerated throughout life. In food allergy (as in any other allergy), this tolerance either does not devel٠٠; or breaks down, so that an innocent food provokes the vigorous defen i\ ...echanisms that normally serve to surround and isolate foreign substances.

As new foods are introduced in infancy and childhood, they are vetted by the discriminating mechanisms of the immune system, which determine whether the response is that of rejection or tolerance. The immune system is particularly vulnerable when it is immature, and it is not uncommon for small infants to develop allergic rather than tolerant reactions to newly introduced foods, especially cows' milk or formula feeds derived from milk. Manufacturers of formula feeds have been aware of this problem for some time and have carried out a great deal of work to minimise the allergenic potential of their products.

With the trend towards early weaning, infants and young children have been exposed to many other foods at an early age, quite apart from cows' milk. An increasing number of food-allergic reactions have been reported at these ages in Western countries, but not universally (see Section 4) - ranging from skin reactions and local inflammation to vomiting and diarrhoea, asthma, or even a life-threatening collapse (anaphylaxis).

In 1993, there were some tragic accidents in which young people died after eating foods that contained nut products, especially peanuts. In nearly all cases, the persons concerned were aware of their intolerance to nuts but were unaware that nuts were present in the food they were eating. There was increasing public concern about these cases, and the Food Minister (Mr Soames) alerted the entire food industry to the need to ensure that all purchasers were made aware of the presence of nuts as a food ingredient. Food allergy, instead of being an unusual quirk of nature, became a high-profile subject, and food manufacturers found themselves having to give serious thought to the allergenic potential of their products.

EPIDEMIOLOGY

There is an extraordinary discrepancy between the scientific evidence about food intolerance of all kinds and the public perception. Kardinal[3] has quoted studies that report a prevalence ranging from 4% to 33% among a surveyed population. He suggests, not unreasonably, that the frequency of self-diagnosis on which these studies were based may be influenced by the extent of recent publicity on food-related reactions. After one particularly emotive televison programme in the UK, a number of general practitioners complained about a substantial influx of patients with self-diagnosed but non-existent allergic disease.

If it is accepted that self-diagnosis may be unreliable, it follows that, whenever possible, the proposed diagnosis should be assessed carefully and confirmed objectively. Studies in England and the Netherlands have attempted to do this by offering a double-blind challenge test (in which both the patient and the administrator are 'blind' to the nature of the food tested) to people with self-diagnosed food intolerance in order to confirm their perceptions. When Young et al.[4] sent questionnaires to one in ten of the people on a local electoral register of 30,000 people, they received replies from 18,582 people, 62% of those canvassed. Of those who replied, 15.6% thought that they had an unpleasant reaction caused by specific foods and 7.4% (often the same people) thought that they reacted to food additives. When challenge tests were carried out, the results were different. Only a minority could be shown to react to food, and reactions to food additives were even less common. Nevertheless, up to 1.8% of the population were thought to suffer from some form of food intolerance, and this was presumed to be an underestimate[5] since not all foods could be tested. For food additives, the discrepancy between perception and proof was greater, and intolerant reactions to food were 100 times more frequent than reactions to naturally occurring food additives. (Sodium metabisulfite, however, was not tested.) It was clear that the public perception of a high prevalence of food reactions - and especially of food additive reactions - was not substantiated by the results of challenge tests.

FOOD ADDITIVES

Although intolerant reactions to food additives are less common than adverse reactions to foods, they have aroused much public debate. In some cases, this has involved vigorous attacks on the food industry for using materials that, the proponents claim, are both unnecessary and harmful. Campaigns have been launched in favour of 'natural' food, sometimes asserting that all additives should be banned. The fact that a loaf of bread or a bottle of wine could not be produced without a substantial number of additives has not deterred the campaigners. Critical attacks upon additives in general have been well publicised, and there is a need for better public awareness of their legitimate purpose - to make a food look, taste or smell better and to improve its texture or keeping qualities.

The questions that have been raised about food additives cannot all be dismissed. Preservatives are important because of their role in food safety and food storage, but sodium metabisulfite and other sulfites can cause reactions in asthmatics that, on rare occasions, can even be fatal.[6] Not all of the additives used industrially are essential, and the case for their use is not always a strong one. Of the many that are in use, however, few have been shown to be capable of causing immune system reactions of the allergic type, which are the main cause of the most severe clinical problems. Nitrites give preserved meats their pink colour, but 20 mg of sodium nitrite can cause headaches, rashes, or intestinal symptoms.[7] The antioxidants butylated hydroxyanisole and hydroxytoluene can exacerbate urticaria in occasional cases.[8] Benzoates and sorbic acid have been claimed to do the same, to exacerbate asthma, or to cause rashes on contact with the skin.[9] Some flavouring substances such as balsam of Peru (not covered by current labelling requirements) can occasionally exacerbate pre-existing eczema.[10] The flavour enhancer monosodium glutamate can have local irritant effects if swallowed in concentrated form but can also cause headaches, bloating, or occasionally, an exacerbation of asthma.[11] From the practical viewpoint, it is therefore generally accepted that sensitive people must be helped to avoid the food additives as well as the foods to which they may react. In recognising this, the European and UK regulatory authorities have required food products to be labelled so that purchasers can have detailed information, not only about the main ingredients and their nutritional significance, but also about the presence of colouring agents, preservatives, antioxidants, emulsifiers, stabilisers, sweeteners, and a number of other agents which are identified by "E" numbers (intended to identify additives that have been tested for safety - see Table 1.II).

TABLE 1.II
Main categories of food additives

E100-180 Food appearance, i.e. colours
E200-321 Keeping properties, i.e. preservatives, antioxidants, acidity regulators
E322-495 Modifiers of consistency or texture, i.e. emulsifiers, stabilisers, thickeners, sweeteners

One of the most frequently repeated claims that have been made concerns tartrazine and other colouring agents and their capacity to cause childhood behaviour disorders. The avoidance of additives appears at best to have a short-lived effect on childhood behaviour,[12] but claims continue to be made that make the subject one of continuing controversy. The problem, however, is that hyperactivity has many causes, which tend to be seriously underestimated or neglected when a simplistic dietary régime is prescribed for a condition that, in the majority of cases, is essentially a psychosocial problem. Repeated blind challenge tests are therefore essential before a food-related behaviour disorder is diagnosed.

PUBLIC HEALTH ASPECTS

Both numerically and as a public health hazard, it is the danger of infected food and of wide outbreaks of food poisoning that causes the greatest concern. In public health terms, food intolerance is a minor hazard compared, for example, with the epidemic infections that occur in areas where food hygiene is poor or where preservatives are not used. The regulatory authorities who are concerned with food safety have accepted that preservatives such as sulfites can cause unpleasant or even dangerous reactions in vulnerable people. In the United States, it is required that their presence is indicated in manufactured foods, and the use of sulfite sprays on fresh fruit, vegetables and salads is now banned.

The reactions caused by other additives are seldom severe, but they, too, have had campaigns directed against their use. In some cases, the arguments have been well accepted - for example in discouraging the use of dyes to provide unnecessary colouring to kippers, haddock, drug capsules, and other items. Indeed, in Sweden, the use of tartrazine has been banned, and increasingly detailed labelling is being required by the regulatory authorities elsewhere. While this labelling may help food shoppers who wish to avoid particular ingredients, the effect can sometimes be perverse. After the introduction of E numbers a survey showed that many housewives believed that all additives were bad but that E numbers were the worst. Public concern, once aroused, has sometimes led to a greatly exaggerated anxiety about food safety.

In responding to some of their more forceful critics and in seeking to allay public anxiety, the regulatory authorities have yet to find a solution that will be useful without imposing impossible burdens on the food industry or, indeed, on those purchasers of food who have to read and understand complex labels if they want information about the nutritional or other aspects of a manufactured food. As devised at present, labels are not required to include all the minor components of a food and cannot therefore help the peanut-allergic individual who may be sensitive even to traces of peanut carried over from a previous food on the same production line.

The regulatory authorities, both in the UK and in Brussels, have now considered whether to require very small quantities of ingredients to be labelled. This is by no means a simple problem, and the regulatory bodies have been made aware of the difficulties that could arise for industry if unrealistic requirements are introduced, not least because of the potential legal hazards if a mistake is made. The use of extended labels are in any case unlikely to please the shopper, who will be faced with an increased burden of information, much of which can only be deciphered with the help of a decoding list. If there is an increasingly complex labelling system, many shoppers will lack both the time and the skill to understand it. While information that is considered to be important could be put into bold print, this too must have its limitations.

An alternative approach to a more elaborate food-labelling system has been promoted by the Leatherhead Food Research Association, using a databank from which lists can be prepared of foods that are free from particular ingredients. This development has been appreciated by shoppers and by the dietitians who may have to give advice on the avoidance of specific foods. It has been taken up by a number of supermarkets and has now spread to other countries. It should be noted, however, that the idea has been criticised by a number of manufacturers, who believe that it may expose consumers to risk and manufacturers to litigation if the ingredients of a particular product are changed or if a product sold under the same name in different countries has different ingredients. It is noteworthy that in over ten years of experience with such lists in the Netherlands and the UK these fears have not been realised. It is, however, impossible to generalise from this experience since there are considerable differences in the legal liabilities in different countries (see Section 5).

One other initiative has been provided by 'The Anaphylaxis Campaign' (Mr David Reading), which collects data and provides valuable information to allergic people.

FOOD INTOLERANCE IN ADULTS

The diagnosis of food intolerance may be relatively simple when symptoms such as lip swelling, sneezing, mouth swelling and itching, skin rash or swelling and irritation, vomiting, diarrhoea, or asthma develop rapidly, because the time relationship to food is relatively easy to recognise. The more delayed reactions such as eczema may be more difficult to identify, and there are still controversies over some of the features such as migraine, behavioural disorders, and joint pains that have been claimed to be associated with food. Claims that chocolate can cause migraine are so frequently made that they are difficult to resist but equally difficult to prove. Much more controversial is the notion that foods - or more particularly, colouring agents - may be responsible for lethargy, malaise, or behaviour disorders in adults as well as children. A number of careful but unsuccessful attempts have been made to establish the validity of these claims by giving the suspect substance in an unrecognisable form, only to find that the symptoms were not reproduced by this method.

Once the diagnosis of food intolerance has been made, the distinction between allergy and other causes of intolerance presents the next problem. Of the symptoms listed above, most suggest an allergic cause until proved otherwise, but symptoms such as vomiting and diarrhoea are so commonly caused in other ways that the presence of allergy should never be assumed. The mechanisms and manifestations therefore need to be considered in more detail.

Food Allergy

Of all the reactions to food, food allergy can be the most dramatic and is the best understood. It usually develops within about an hour (eczema being the exception) and involves an unpleasant response of the body surfaces or the linings of the nose, lungs, mouth, stomach, or intestine, so that it can affect almost every system of the body (see Table 1.III). When all the body surfaces react together, the affected person can become very ill with a reaction (anaphylaxis), which involves a general discharge of histamine and other active chemicals from vast numbers of sensitised cells (mast cells). In the worst cases, this leads to spasm of the lung airways, a fall in blood pressure, coma and even death. As with other types of allergic response, it is often made worse by incidental factors such as exercise.[13]

TABLE 1.III
Clinical effects of food allergy

Vomiting, colic, diarrhoea, constipation (occasionally caused by cows' milk)
Sneezing and an obstructed or running nose, cough, asthma
Hives (urticaria), skin swellings (angioedema), eczema
Irritability and sleep disturbances in children, headache
Anaphylaxis in severe cases

Mast cells are the key to immediate allergic reactions of this type. They are dispersed throughout the body, especially below the body surfaces, and they are capable of providing a very powerful, rapid reaction to an external threat. These cells are packed with inflammation-provoking chemicals (see Fig. 1.1), and their surfaces are primed to react specifically to agents that range from bacteria, viruses, and parasites to grass pollen (in hay fever sufferers) and food proteins. The priming agent on the cell surface is a protein "antibody", which is derived from immunoglobulin E (IgE) and reacts specifically with a foreign substance (antigen or allergen) to which the body has been exposed. Once it has been formed elsewhere in the body by B lymphocytes, IgE enters the bloodstream and homes onto the surface of mast cells, where it can detect the presence of even trace amounts of allergen. If even a few molecules of antibody and allergen combine on the mast cell surface, this triggers the release of histamine and other inflammatory substances, which in turn mobilise other protective mechanisms. The result is a cascading series of 'protective' responses, which can be self-damaging or even dangerous if they are directed against harmless foods rather than an invading microorganism.

1.   **The production of IgE antibodies**
[The lymphocyte (B cell), which produces various types of immunoglobulin (Ig)]

2.   **Their attachment to mast cells**
[The mast cell, packed with histamine and other chemical mediators]

3.   **The allergen latches on**

4.   **The mast cell is activated - histamine is released**

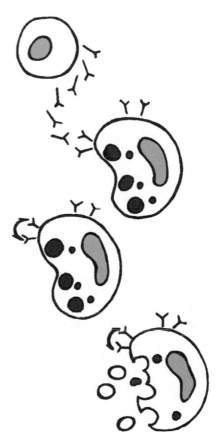

Fig. 1.1 Activation of mast cells

Not all immunological reactions to food are of the immediate allergic type. Coeliac disease is thought to depend on a delayed hypersensitivity reaction to wheat gluten, which involves other white blood cells (T lymphocytes). The manufacturer's concerns about the gluten content of food are considered in detail in Section 5.

Toxic Food Reactions

Poisoning from contaminated food is usually easily distinguished from food intolerance, since it often occurs as part of an outbreak and there is no history of past episodes triggered in quite the same way. Repeated symptoms of food intolerance can, however, be provoked by foods that contain naturally occurring toxins such as the solanidine that is present in some potatoes, the haemagglutinins in undercooked red kidney beans, protease inhibitors in soya, or toxic alkaloids in shellfish that have fed on dinoflagellates and plankton.[14] The mechanism - a direct toxic effect - is quite different from that of food allergy, although in some cases the clinical end result can be very similar. Life-threatening reactions - for example, to toadstools - are not unknown, and there can also be serious toxic effects from inhaled sulfur dioxide when sodium metabisulfite is the preservative used and the food is ingested by an asthmatic subject.

Pharmacological Effects

There is a tendency to underestimate the drug-like effects of some components of food, including histamine in wine and badly stored fish. The effects of histamine and of other biologically active amines include flushing and skin rashes. A much more common pharmacological effect, however, is that of caffeine - an important feature of everyday life in those who use this highly addictive substance. Since there is 60 mg of caffeine in a cup of tea and 100 mg in an average cup of coffee, the potentially toxic level of 250 mg is easily exceeded in the heavy coffee drinker. Even cola drinks can contain up to 60 mg of caffeine. The ability of caffeine to stimulate mental activity and reduce fatigue are well known, but it can also provoke nervousness, irritability, agitation, tremor and headache. Heavy coffee drinkers may sleep poorly and complain of palpitations, nausea, vomiting, abdominal pain, and changes in bowel habit. Paradoxically, sudden caffeine withdrawal may lead to a temporary exacerbation of nearly all these symptoms, in which case any attempts to reduce the caffeine intake may have to be phased.

Enzyme Deficiencies

If foodstuffs are not digested they often remain unabsorbed. If that happens, they pass through, unchanged, to the lower bowel, where they are broken down and fermented by bacteria and cause bloating, diarrhoea and abdominal pain. This is what happens in the very common deficiency of the enzyme lactase, which is normally responsible for the breakdown of lactose, the sugar present in milk. Some babies are born with a lactase deficiency, leading to diarrhoea, which may be confused with cows' milk allergy. Much more commonly, however, this condition manifests itself in adult life. Up to 90% of many adult communities - for example in Africa - have a deficiency in lactase. Those who are affected develop diarrhoea and bloating after taking cows' milk, but not after consuming live yoghurt, in which much of the lactose has been broken down. Whether this reaction should be regarded as abnormal is another matter. It has been suggested that the loss of this enzyme in adult life may be normal, indicating that man is not 'designed' to continue to take milk after early childhood.

Other types of sugar intolerance are much less common, but an inability to metabolise galactose or fructose has been an occasional cause of severe illness, especially in infancy.

FOODS IMPLICATED

The most common foods causing intolerant reactions are listed in Table 1.IV, but in spite of its wide range the list cannot be regarded as complete. The main foods that are capable of causing severe allergic reactions have been indicated, the most dangerous in recent years being nuts and peanuts. It should be noted, however, that life-threatening reactions can also occur through non-allergic mechanisms (as in reactions to sulfite preservatives).

Some of the foods that provoke allergy can also cause other types of food reaction. As noted, cows' milk can cause an allergic response, but symptoms can also arise in lactase deficiency, owing to excessive fermentation of unabsorbed lactose in the large bowel. Wheat can cause allergic reactions as well as the delayed reactions of gluten sensitivity (coeliac disease), but it can also cause diarrhoea in people who are not gluten-sensitive. It is not possible, therefore, to categorise foods according to their ability to cause allergic reactions as opposed to other types of food intolerance.

TABLE 1.IV

Foods causing food intolerance

Commonly involved
Cows' milk (and other milks)*, egg*, nuts* and peanuts*, fish*, soya bean*
Wheat (and other cereals and yeast)*, coffee and tea, chocolate, citrus fruit, chick peas and rice (in Asian countries)

Other foods
Sulfite preservatives (mainly in asthmatics) and other food additives
Aniseed, apple*, artichoke, banana*, beans (various), beetroot, berries (various), buckwheat*, camomile, celery*, chestnut, chicken, chicory, fennel, garlic and onion, gelatin, ginger, herbs, honey, hops, horseradish, kiwifruit, lychees, mango, millet, mushroom, mustard*, sesame*, other seeds and spices, nutmeg, peas, peppers, potato, soft fruits (including grapes and raisins*), sweet potato, tapioca, vanilla.

* Recognised causes of severe allergic reactions

A number of the 'allergenic' components of food have now been identified and isolated,[15] both for animal foods (cows' milk, chicken, eggs, cod, shrimp) and for plants (peanut, Brazil nut, mustard, soya bean, wheat). The allergens that cause these reactions are usually proteins, and in the case of cows' milk these are mainly the lactoglobulins and caseins rather than the immunoglobulins or lactalbumin. Although beta-lactoglobulin accounts for only 10% of the total protein, it is the only protein type that is not present in human milk and is a potent allergen for the young infant. It is resistant to acid digestion in the stomach and is therefore more likely to reach the small intestine intact, which may perhaps make it more likely to be 'recognised' as a foreign substance.

While the identification of food antigens has helped in the understanding of the process of sensitisation, it has failed to solve the problem of preventing or treating individual sensitivities. One of the reasons is that each food contains more than one allergenic protein - usually several - and allergic people react to each one of these proteins to a different extent. No single protein could therefore be used for the purpose of desensitisation.

In analysing food-allergic reactions, cross-sensitisation provides a further problem, because of the molecular similarity between proteins of similar biological origin. In the Scandinavian countries, it is well recognised that people who have hay fever provoked by pollen from the silver birch tree may be allergic to the soft fruit of several other trees[16] or may even be sensitive to manufactured food products containing soya flour. Allergy to another tree product - latex rubber - can also be associated with allergy to fruits, especially, in this case, bananas and chestnuts.[17] With the increased use of latex for household gloves and for medical purposes, this type of allergy appears to be increasing. Other cross-reactions have led people who are allergic to birch or mugwort pollen to develop an allergy to celery, and ragweed- sensitive people in the United States may also react to melon and banana.

For the food manufacturer, it is often the foods which are present as minor components that are the most likely to cause problems. Patients who are sensitive to soya may quickly learn to avoid botanically related legumes such as peas, beans and lentils. They may find it more difficult, however, to identify the soya that has been incorporated into such products as cereal mixtures, soups, sauces, biscuits, baked foods, or infant formula feeds.

DIAGNOSIS

The investigation of illness caused by food often starts with the possibility of food contamination or infection, so that this must be excluded as a first step. The patient's history is therefore crucial before any investigations are carried out. When the story clearly suggests that there is a repeated intolerance to an uncontaminated food, the next step, where possible, is to withdraw the suspect food for a 2- to 3-week period, followed by a 'challenge' test to establish that a similar reaction occurs even when the subject cannot identify the food that has been given. Ideally, a series of double-blind, placebo-controlled food challenges (DBPCFC) are given (see above), in which the given substance may be either a food or an inert placebo. The 'DBPCFC' is often cited as the diagnostic gold standard, but it may be inappropriate when there has been a florid, well-observed potentially dangerous reaction. Here, the history alone may have to suffice, sometimes coupled with skin tests carried out under close medical supervision (usually with egg, fish or nuts). Other laboratory methods, though frequently offered commercially as diagnostic tests, are never able to prove that food allergy is present. Even in the presence of a positive skin or blood test for IgE antibodies, there may be no evidence of a clinical sensitivity.

Double-blind challenge tests may be unduly demanding in the most common problem of infancy, which is cows' milk intolerance. In infancy and early childhood, it is usual to accept open testing under close medical supervision.

In the older infant a number of foods can cause allergic reactions, but the most common problems that arise are concerned with the food that is usually the first to be introduced on weaning - cows' milk. It should be appreciated that allergy should not, however, be the chief suspect when an infant develops symptoms. If diarrhoea is the main feature, there is a variety of blood and stool tests that help to exclude other causes, for example in identifying lactase deficiency. If vomiting is the only symptom, allergy is unlikely, since air swallowing and vomiting may arise from simple causes - such as feeding from a bottle that has too small a hole in the teat.

As in other types of food intolerance, an important step towards diagnosis is the elimination of the suspect food, in this case by changing to some type of formula feed for up to a 2- to 3-week period - if necessary, excluding cows' milk derivatives entirely. If improvement occurs, a re-challenge with gradually increasing quantities of milk is arranged, under careful hospital supervision. A recurrence of symptoms is not a complete proof of the diagnosis, but if a withdrawal of milk is again followed by improvement there is a need to find a well-tolerated substitute for at least six months before a re-challenge with the same strict precautions.

FOOD INTOLERANCE IN INFANCY AND CHILDHOOD

Milk Allergy

The food manufacturer who produces milk-based or other food products for infants must accept the inevitable - that no product will be acceptable to every child and that occasional adverse reactions are almost impossible to avoid. Infants have a relatively immature immune system and are particularly likely to develop inappropriate allergic reactions, which are not necessarily long-lasting but can be both difficult to recognise and awkward to manage. While allergy or intolerance to cows' milk and cows' milk products should not be diagnosed too readily, they are relatively common and probably affect over 2% of the childhood population.[18] It is vital, however, that the diagnosis should not be made too lightly since, once embarked upon, the subsequent dietary régime may cause a considerable disturbance to the life of the entire family, with a lengthy and difficult period of supervision, followed, in due course, by laborious attempts to reintroduce milk.

Babies with both a family history of allergy and a high level of IgE in their blood have an increased tendency to develop some form of allergy, and cows' milk allergy in particular. Some are sensitised from birth, but the most common story is of the development of diarrhoea a week or so after cows' milk has been introduced or else, at a later date, the development of skin itching and eczema, irritability and sleep disturbance. In other cases, all is well until the chance development of an acute intestinal infection, an event that is known to be capable of causing cell damage[19] and which is sometimes followed by the development of cows' milk allergy. Infants who are sensitive to cows' milk also have a 38% chance of developing allergy to other foods (especially eggs) and almost a 50% chance of developing hay fever or asthma.[20] For all of these reasons, a continuation of breast feeding for several months, and a late introduction of cows' milk are recommended as the best way to diminish the risk of cows' milk sensitisation. Soya-protein preparations have also been used, with varying success, both in the prevention and treatment of cows' milk protein intolerance (see below), but these preparations have themselves led to reactions in some cases.[21]

While it is clear that genetic factors may increase the likelihood of an allergic reaction, other factors are also important. One of these is the age at which a food is first encountered. Reactions to cows' milk are thus seen at an earlier age than reactions to other foods, which are, traditionally, introduced later on (see Fig. 1.2).

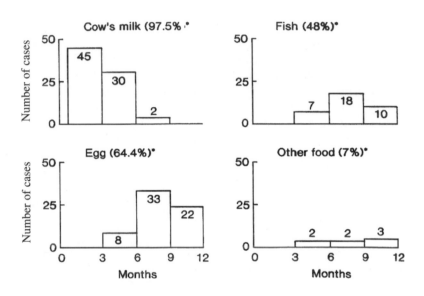

* % of all cases with this allergy presenting in first year

Fig. 2. The development of food allergies in the first 3, 6, 9 and 12 months of life (Data derived from Esteban[22])

Treatment

Milk allergy is important not only because of its frequency but also because of the difficulties that can arise when alternative feeds are required. Cows' milk has more protein and other solutes than human milk, an unbalanced pattern of amino acids, and insufficient iron, zinc, essential fatty acids, and vitamins C and D. It should not be given to infants below the age of 6 months because the infant kidney cannot deal with the high mineral content, and an overload of phosphate may lead to dehydration and also a fall in serum calcium levels. Its nutritional value, however, is great. Consumption of 500 ml of cows' milk daily can provide half the protein and all the fat, water, calcium and riboflavin that a 2-year-old child requires, together with a quarter of the recommended energy intake.

When devising cows'-milk-based formulae for infants and children, the food industry has taken account of these reservations. Preparations of cows' milk, even for healthy children, have been modified in their casein:whey ratio. Vitamin D and iron have been added, with a mixture of vegetable and animal fats to boost the level of essential fatty acids and increase fat absorption. It should be noted, however, that preparations of this kind are not always trouble-free. For example, an allergic reaction has been reported to an infant formula containing peanut oil, which proved to be due to allergy to peanut protein.[23]

In cows' milk protein intolerance, formulae that rely on unmodified protein are not appropriate. Other animal milk products have been tried but are seldom tolerated because of cross-reactivity between their proteins and those of cows' milk. Furthermore, the danger of an unbalanced feed is always present, as, for example, with goats' milk, which has a very high mineral content, a high iron content, and a relative deficiency of vitamin C. The milk substitutes that are most commonly used are therefore those based on protein hydrolysates made from casein, whey, or meat, or else on soya proteins. They have to be easily available, cheap and palatable, and must contain all the necessary nutrients. While milk and soya hydrolysates are the most common, the successful use of meat-based formulae has attracted sufficient commercial interest to see the development of mixed soya and collagen hydrolysates and of a chicken preparation supplemented by glucose polymer and vegetable oil.

Hydrolysates of milk

Infant formulae based on heat-denatured and enzymically hydrolysed milk proteins have been in use for several decades. The average molecular weight of the final constituents range from 100-6,000 for the more hydrolysed preparations. The less hydrolysed formulae may have a mean molecular weight of 15,000 and contain sufficient undenatured protein to be unsuitable for cows' milk-allergic infants. One of the most stringent tests of these 'hypoallergenic' formulae is in the treatment of an infant who is already sensitised, but they have also been used to reduce the risk of sensitisation in the infants of allergic parents. Preparations containing protease-digested casein, for example, tend to produce a very mild response in sensitive subjects. They vie mainly with soya protein preparations, and, provided that these are suitably fortified for the child or infant, they also provide adequate nutrition. Apart from a minority of infants who are sensitised, they are generally well accepted.

Strategies have been developed for different types of enzymic proteolysis of milk proteins, which split the molecule at points where specific amino acids are placed. It must be acknowledged, however, that enzyme residues can themselves provoke an allergic response. As the amino acids lysine and arginine are well distributed over the chain, cleaving the protein at these sites by porcine trypsin results in well distributed cuts over the entire length of some major protein molecules.[24] When processed in this way, the larger fragments still appear to be allergenic but the smallest fragments are completely unreactive. Allergenic potential may thus be virtually abolished by thorough enzymic breakdown. The resulting hydrolysates may be remarkably unpalatable, and the search continues for preparations that are both acceptable and cheap.

FOOD INTOLERANCE IN OLDER CHILDREN

When the management of food intolerance is considered, the problem in infancy is substantially greater than that in older children. By the age of 2 years, these problems are more manageable, since there are no foods that cannot be replaced, albeit with difficulty. When cows' milk does not itself have to be excluded, it can provide protein, calories, calcium and riboflavin. Meat, vegetables, fish and fruit provide a wide range of other options, as they do for children who have to rely on gluten-free products or rice and potatoes because of an intolerance to wheat or gluten. Because of the dangers of an unbalanced diet, the advice of a dietitian is needed in all these cases. It is in these circumstances that the availability of food databanks has been of particular value.

PROSPECTS FOR THE FUTURE

One of the disappointments in the management of food intolerance has been the failure of medical attempts at desensitisation or reliable pharmacological control. While the injection of adrenaline can be lifesaving, and corticosteroids, antihistamines and anti-diarrhoeal agents can all help, the progress of drug treatment has been disappointingly slow. Genetic engineering, exciting though it is in concept, has also been slow to make headway in its attempts to eliminate allergenic proteins from rice or cereal grains. The current management of problems therefore depends largely on the avoidance of suspect foods, helped by measures that identify food ingredients in manufactured products. It is the latter that presents the most immediate challenge for food manufacturers. The problem does not concern only current products. With the introduction of novel foods and of bioindustrial enzymes into food processing, there is also the possibility that new allergies may develop. Food manufacturers therefore need to find ways of defining the major and minor components of their own products, to include not only regular ingredients but also those that are occasionally present. There is then the question of how best to indicate their presence in order to meet the rising expectations of the regulatory authorities and the public.

REFERENCES

1.   Discovering the causes of atopy.
     Shaheen S.
     British Medical Journal, 1997, 314, 987-8.

2.   Food intolerance and food aversion.
     Royal College of Physicians and British Nutrition Foundation.
     Journal of the Royal College of Physicians London, 1984, 18, 83-123.

3.   Epidemiology of Food Allergy and Food Intolerance.
     Kardinaal AFM.
     In: Food Allergy and Food Intolerance. Ed JC Somogyi, IIR Muller, Th Ockhuizen.
     Bibliotheca Nutritio et Dieta. Karger, Basel. 1991. No.48. pp105-15.

4.   The prevalence of reactions to food additives in a survey population.
      Young E, Patel S, Stoneham M *et al.*
      Journal of the Royal College of Physicians London, 1987, 21, 241-7.

5.   Food Intolerance.
      Young E.
      Lancet, 1994, 344, 137-8.

6.   Adverse reactions to food and drug additives.
      Simon RA. In: Progress in Allergy and Clinical Immunology.
      Eds Pichler WJ, Stadler BM, Dahinden CE.
      Hografe and Huber, Toronto, 1989, 467-70.

7.   Le rôle du nitrite de sodium dans les urticaures histaminique d'origine
      alimentaire.
      Moneret-Vautrin DA, Einhorn C, Tisserand J.
      Ann Nutr Aliment, 1980, 34, 1125-32.

8.   Chronic urticaria exacerbated by antioxidant food preservatives, butylated
      hydroxyanisole (BHA) and butylated hydroxytoluene (BHT).
      Goodman MD, McDonnell JT, Nelson HS *et al.*
      Journal of Allergy and clinical Immunology 1990, 86, 570-5.

9.   Adverse reactions to benzoates and parabens.
      Jacobsen DW. In: Food Allergy: Adverse Reactions to Foods and Food
      Additives. Eds Metcalfe DD, Sampson HA, Simon RA.
      Blackwell Scientific Publications, Boston. 1991, 278-82.

10.   Oral challenge with balsam of Peru.
      Veien NK.
      Contact Dermatitis, 1985, 12, 104-7.

11.   Monosodium glutamate.
      Allen DH. In: Food Allergy: Adverse Reactions to Foods and Food
      Additives. Eds Metcalfe DD, Sampson HA, Simon RA.
      Blackwell Scientific Publications, Boston. 1991, 263-6.

12.   Reactions to dietary tartrazine.
      David TJ.
      Archives of Diseases of Childhood, 1987, 62, 119-22.

13.   Food-dependent, exercise-induced anaphylaxis: A study on 11 Japanese
      cases. Dohi M, Suko M, Sugiyama H et al.
      Journal of Allergy and Clinical Immunology 1991, 87, 34-40.

14. Food and food additive intolerance in childhood.
    David TJ.
    Blackwell Scientific Publications, Oxford, 1993.

15. Food Allergens.
    Bush RK, Hefle SL.
    Clinical Reviews in Food Science and Nutrition, 1996, 36(S), S119-163.

16. Immunological partial identity between pollen and food allergens.
    Halmepuro L, Bjorksten F.
    Allergy, 1985, 3, 70-1.

17. Latex allergy in patient allergic to fruit
    Lavaud F, Cossart C, Reiter V, et al.
    Lancet 1992, 339, 492-3 (and following page).

18. Prevalence of soy allergy in young children with cow milk allergy
    (Abstract). Sampson HA, Zeiger RS, Bock SA, et al.
    Journal of Allergy and Clinical Immunology, 1997, 99, S491.

19. Milk protein enteropathy after acute infectious gastroenteritis: experimental
    and clinical observations.
    Kleinman RE.
    Journal of Pediatrics 1991, 118, 5111-5.

20. A prospective study of cow's milk allergy in Danish infants during the first
    three years of life. Clinical course in relation to clinical and immunological
    type of hypersensitivity reaction.
    Host A, Halken S.
    Allergy 1990, 45, 487-96.

21. Efficacy and safety of a soy-protein-formula for feeding babies with atopic
    dermatitis and cow's milk hypersensitivity.
    Cantani A, Ferrara M, Ragno V, Businco L.
    European Reviews of Meidicine and Pharmacological Science, 1990, 12,
    311-8.

22. Advances in food reactions in childhood: concept, importance, and present
    problems.
    Esteban M.
    Journal of Pediatrics, 1992, 121, S1-3.

23 L'allergie à la cachuete chez le nourisson: le danger de certain laits
   maternises.
   Hatahet R, Kanny G, Moneret-Vautrin DA.
   Revue Française d'Allergologie, 1992, 32, 86-7.

24.   Whey protein allergenicity and its reduction by technological means.
       Jost R, Monti JC, Pahud JJ.
       Food Technology 1987, 41, 118-21.

2. PRACTICAL MANAGEMENT IN THE FOOD INDUSTRY - A CASE STUDY

Neville Craddock

INTRODUCTION

The question of food intolerance has received considerable public, scientific and medical scrutiny during the past few years. Since 1993, a number of fatalities from peanut-induced anaphylaxis have occurred and a further substantial number of non-fatal cases have been reported. Similar serious reactions have also been caused by several other foodstuffs such as molluscs, fish, eggs, milk and soya.

Although many investigations have been carried out in attempts to define the basis of the allergic reaction, to define the nature of the causative proteins, and to quantify the amount of allergen necessary to trigger a reaction in sensitive persons, it remains the case that the only sure way in which an adverse reaction can be averted is the total avoidance of the allergenic foods or foods containing them.

In the UK, at the present time, the principal focus of attention has been peanuts and other nut derivatives, but, at an international level, there is much discussion on a wider list of foodstuffs and their derivatives known, or alleged, to cause hypersensitivity in susceptible persons.

In practice, it seems that the number of potential allergens and individual, adverse reactions to food components is enormous and one is tempted to suggest that it would be impossible to anticipate all the potential reactions that could arise. Certainly, it is clear that no single system of communicating to customers, e.g. labelling alone, could comprehensively address the situation.

This chapter will focus on the problems caused by peanuts in particular, and other nuts in general. It will describe how Nestlé UK Ltd has assessed the legal, commercial and practical issues involved and how the Company is implementing a policy to address what are believed to be our legal and moral obligations.

It must be emphasised that no single action by a food manufacturer can solve the problem for all individual susceptible consumers but, in conjunction with the efforts of others such as schools, government, the medical profession and specific interest groups, a major contribution in this area can be made.

LEGAL BACKGROUND

It is a fundamental requirement that all food manufacturers, caterers and retailers be responsible for ensuring that any food that they supply is safe to eat, is fit for the purpose intended and is labelled in accordance with specific, relevant legislation. However, in addition to the various elements of food legislation, whether in the UK or elsewhere, it is necessary to consider the implications of relevant consumer protection legislation, general principles of civil legislation and Common Law and, in particular, requirements arising from the European Product Liability and Product Safety Directives.

These obligations to comply with criminal and civil law require all manufacturers to consider the extent to which their position, and that of their products, will be influenced by the following circumstances. Such assessments will need to be reviewed on a regular basis, dependent upon developments in any or all of them as time progresses.

In the UK and several other countries around the world, a significant number of people have died or been seriously affected as a direct result of an allergic reaction following ingestion of foodstuffs that, unbeknown to them, contained low levels of, for example, peanuts or peanut derivatives. These cases have received widespread publicity and it is now a fact that the scientific community, the food industry and a sizeable proportion of the general public are fully aware that a number of common foods and food ingredients can give rise to rapid, life-threatening reactions in a small number of sensitised people.

Even though these cases have been mainly, if not entirely, limited to non-prepacked foodstuffs for which it is impossible to know exactly what information was available to the consumer at the time of their purchase, it is very difficult for any responsible food manufacturer to deny knowledge, today, of the existence of this problem.

Although there is no agreed, definitive list of these life-threatening allergens, there is a general, widespread agreement over the identity of up to ten materials that give rise to serious cause for concern.

A second consideration is that already, in the UK, several large food companies, including the major retailers, have started voluntary labelling of their products to indicate either the known presence or the possible adventitious presence of certain allergens, in particular nuts and nut derivatives. Routine evaluation and comparison of competitors' products by a manufacturer will therefore bring this labelling to his attention, thereby further weakening any suggestion that he may be unaware of the existence of the problem of food allergenicity.

The UK Government has recommended to industry, including caterers and retailers of loose products, that they should indicate the known or potential presence of peanuts and similar materials in the foods which they sell. This practice is becoming increasingly prevalent in a number of commercial outlets and even staff restaurants.

In 1995, the European Commission asked the Scientific Committee for Foodstuffs to examine the question of food allergenicity and to give an Opinion. The SCF Report examined, in some detail, the numerical and geographic prevalence of adverse reactions to various foods and food ingredients but did not go so far as to recommend any widely applicable mechanisms on how industry could, or should, address the problem.

Within the EU, a number of Member States are beginning to address the issue with varying degrees of official recommendations on food labelling aspects.

Early in 1997, the European Commission issued a draft proposal to amend the labelling directive in such a way that current exemptions from labelling for certain food ingredients will not apply in the case of a list of materials recognised as causing allergic reactions or intolerances. The list of foodstuffs and ingredients is broadly in line with that of other organisations except for the omission of milk and milk products; however, this is believed to be an accidental omission.

Codex Alimentarius is currently considering a similar change to its General Standard for Labelling of Prepackaged Foods to include a mandatory list of foods and ingredients that are known to cause hypersensitivity and which should always be declared. This proposal, currently at Step 3 of the Codex procedure, was discussed in Ottawa during April 1997 but it is understood that little progress was made. In France, the authorities have recently published a detailed review of the situation and recommended a number of ways in which industry, collectively, can significantly improve the information given to consumers. Again, a restricted list of potential allergens is covered, but the principal focus is on peanuts and similar derivatives, coupled with clearly defined changes to the legal framework of labelling.

In Sweden, labelling legislation requires that ingredients that are known to be capable of causing hypersensitivity reactions are always stated in the list of ingredients. Examples quoted include eggs, milk, gluten-containing grains and legumes such as soya beans, peas and peanuts. The Swedish legislation also requires that, when such ingredients are themselves present in compound foodstuffs, any exemptions from ingredient declaration do not apply.

In view of the developments - and notwithstanding that the majority of responsible food manufacturers wish to establish the most appropriate means of assisting potential victims - it is pertinent to consider what are the overall legal obligations to inform prospective purchasers of the known or adventitious presence of certain allergens, even where this is not a specific requirement of current food labelling legislation, whether any liability arises from unknown or unsuspected presence, and, in the case of any incident, from which Statutes such liability might arise. Additionally, it becomes necessary to consider how best a manufacturer might be able to discharge his responsibilities in the cases of widely differing commercial circumstances; is it appropriate that all relevant indications should be given in the ingredients list or is an alternative location required - or should the information even be on a label at all? If indications are to be given on labels, how prominent should they be - and do different circumstances merit different treatments even by the same manufacturer?

It is clear that, where an ingredient is knowingly added to a food, the Food Labelling Regulations 1996 require that such presence should be declared in the ingredients list. There are, however, certain exemptions to this general rule: where the ingredient is itself part of a compound ingredient that is present in the final foodstuff at less than 25%, only the name of the compound ingredient need be given; also, specified generic terms may also be used, for example in the case of vegetable oils. Further exemptions also apply where the material has performed the role of a "processing aid" during the manufacture of a foodstuff but no longer performs any significant function in the end product. Equally, there is no statutory obligation under food labelling legislation or other criminal law to declare materials whose presence may be purely adventitious as a result of the method or location of manufacture, as opposed to deliberate and known addition to the product.

In the case of adventitious presence of an ingredient provoking an allergic response in a product, there may be a potential offence under Sections 14 and 15 of the Food Safety Act 1990 and possibly under the General Product Safety Regulations 1994. Recently, Local Authorities Co-ordinating Body on Trading Standards (LACOTS), advised by the Department of Health, suggested that any such instances becoming known to enforcement authorities should be treated under the official food hazard warning system, whereby all local authorities are automatically notified of potential problems.

However, of greater concern perhaps to a responsible manufacturer and with regard to potential civil litigation, is that he could possibly be deemed to have been negligent under the Consumer Protection Act 1987. In order to avoid potential civil litigation, it would therefore be necessary for a manufacturer to show that some 'duty of care' had been demonstrated by making the presence of such an ingredient known to anyone who might need to be aware of it.

In all the statutes referred to above, a form of due diligence defence is available to the manufacturer. On the other hand, in view of the recent publicity surrounding these issues and the ongoing debate in many quarters, it is likely that the level of diligence required could well be substantial and any defence offered would be subject to intense scrutiny.

The question of how best to address the situation from a manufacturing viewpoint and how best to advise potential customers via labelling or other routes is one that has generated a great deal of discussion within the food industry. Accepting that some form of notification is required, the basic question then hinges on whether it is sufficient for the presence or possible presence of a potentially life-threatening allergen to be mentioned in the ingredients list (and if so how) or whether a greater prominence on the label might be required - and, if so, under what circumstances ?

On the one hand, it can clearly be argued that allergic individuals represent a rather specialised case and they therefore owe themselves a particular 'duty of care'. They themselves might therefore be expected to exercise more than the usual level of diligence and might be expected to scrutinise food labels rather more closely than the average consumer. It would follow from this that a reference to a potential allergen in, or adjacent to, the ingredients list would in most cases be quite adequate. However, it could equally be argued that such a mechanism might not be sufficient in those cases where similarly branded products are available, or existing ranges are extended. It might also be insufficient when otherwise apparently identical (in the minds of the consumer) products are produced under different factory conditions or, potentially one of the most difficult and dangerous cases, when products available in different countries have been produced under "safe" conditions in one country but are subject to a quantifiable risk of adventitious contamination with a potential allergen when produced in one or more other locations.

This problem should not be underestimated. The progressive development of the European Single Market is leading to an increasing number of products, sold with multilingual labels, having been produced in one central "European" factory, and being for sale in a number of countries simultaneously. This situation is not confined to large multinational manufacturers; increasingly, we see the major retailers selling products with European labels. Furthermore, there is an increasing trend, certainly in other European countries, for the average consumer to be able to read and understand basic food information in more than one language. If it is considered necessary to advise, for example, the British (or English-speaking) consumers of potential dangers for a particular product, can it be considered reasonable not to advise those reading the label, in, say, Dutch, French, German, Italian or Spanish?

However, by far the majority of products sold in a given country still carry the labelling only in the single national language. Nevertheless, this leads to a further question: if allergy "warning statements" are appearing on some multilingual imported products in these countries, is it then reasonable for similar statements not to appear on national, monolingual labels for similar products?

Clearly, such deliberations are fundamental to any decisions that a manufacturer must make for his own products, but they also demonstrate how the actions of one manufacturer may influence the decisions of others in his own country, and even the extent to which the actions of a manufacturer in one country may also have a substantial influence on the decisions and actions that may need to be taken in other countries.

Discussions on food allergenicity issues, both within and outside our industry over the past 3 years have shown that the UK consideration of this complex issue is well ahead of that of most other countries.

THE NESTLÉ APPROACH

Within Nestlé UK Ltd, we have been very conscious of the problems that can be caused by allergenic foods, for two principal reasons. Firstly, our international interest in nutrition and the work carried out at the Nestlé Research Centre in Lausanne, Switzerland, allows us to claim to be one of the world's leading nutrition-based companies. Indeed, we have been pioneers in the development, particularly, of hypo-allergenic infant feeds. Secondly, our international trading base allows us to respond to, and build constructively upon, issues such as allergenicity wherever in the world they may occur. Specifically, our first UK experience of the peanut allergy problem arose many years ago from the manufacture and labelling of certain confectionery products, manufactured in the UK for the North American market and requiring a "nut warning statement" on the export packaging.

Our current policy on peanut, or to be more precise, nut and peanut allergy has therefore been developed and refined over a period of several years. Although we are aware that it may be considered by some parties to be excessive, we do not think so; we believe we have taken a realistic and practical view of the various problems confronting us.

We consider as falling within our nut allergy policy not only peanuts and their derivatives but also walnuts, hazelnuts, almonds and Brazils; we deliberately include all the nut oils, regardless of their degree of refinement, on a safety-first basis, whilst recognising that ongoing research might change this situation. Recent work carried out in Southampton seems to indicate that highly refined peanut oil may not present problems for patients known to be at risk from normal peanut allergens. However, such work cannot address the real-life situation for a manufacturer whereby the risk of cross-contamination of highly refined oils with other less pure materials needs to be fully investigated before the manufacturer's products themselves may be said to present no risk to susceptible consumers.

In recognition of this, the Seed Crushers and Oil Processors Association has recently formulated a Code of Practice for its members, recommending that, where any risk of cross-contamination of refined oils may arise, such oils should carry an appropriate allergen statement when sold to manufacturers for the purpose of their business or sold by retail, direct to consumers.

Our Nestlé UK policy on nut usage in products is clear: we will only use nuts and nut derivatives in those products in which they may reasonably be expected to be present; where alternative raw materials are available, for example as functional ingredients, we will use "nut-free" options.

All aspects of raw material composition, the production process, product recipes (including any rework options that may exist within or between product lines and factories), product handling and packaging are evaluated; guidance is issued to factory and site restaurants and, in those locations where peanut material is handled, we place clear statements at the reception area to alert all visitors to the site to this effect.

All products and processing are subject to a full HACCP-type (Hazard Analysis Critical Control Point) analysis in order to establish whether there is a risk of any nut material being present in a finished product and what this risk might be. This will identify any risk of either individual, small pieces or accumulative, fine-powder doses of allergen potentially resulting in cross-contamination to or from other products and the steps that need to be taken to prevent it. In addition to the obvious aspects, such as products made using common equipment and the possible options for rework included in a given recipe, particular attention is also paid to such aspects as clean-in-place procedures, air flows within and between different parts of the buildings, and containers in which materials are used and stored, for example bulk bags.

All compound ingredients that may contain nut derivatives, either directly or indirectly, are checked, e.g. blended fats and oils, carriers, flavourings, pre-mixes, hydrolysed proteins, etc. In addition to the obvious requests for information and assurances from suppliers, regular audits of their premises and operations are carried out.

All procedures are fully documented as part of the factory Quality Management System procedures; we consider this to be essential in the event that Nestlé should be required to defend itself at any point in the future.

Any products that are considered to have a potential presence of any nut material or to be at risk from cross-contamination from processing, packaging or reworking will bear a reference to this on the label. If appropriate, consideration will be given to range rationalisation, in order to eliminate unnecessary risks. Detailed labelling rules are in place, according to the origin of the inclusion, or potential inclusion, of the allergen.

If the presence is due to the known or deliberate inclusion of an allergen, either directly or as a result of a rework recipe, a declaration by specific name of the particular ingredient will be made in the appropriate position in the ingredients list. Where the presence may arise from adventitious and unavoidable, but very low-frequency or low-risk cross-contamination, a statement to the effect that a product "may contain nut traces" will appear immediately following the ingredients list.

In addition, depending upon the nature of the product, a specific reference may be made to the allergen, e.g. peanuts, in the name of the food or the detailed product description if appropriate.

Current food labelling legislation at national and European level contains various legal exemptions from the mandatory declaration of ingredients under specific conditions. It has been Nestlé's policy for several years to ignore these. Where we know that nut derivatives are present in the product (for whatever reason) we have deliberately chosen to ignore the so-called "25% rule", whereby the components of a compound food ingredient may be exempt from declaration; we therefore declare all nut derivatives in their appropriate position in the ingredients list. Compound ingredients are either exploded into their component parts and declared separately or the presence of the specific allergen is indicated in brackets after the name of the compound ingredient. A similar procedure has been in place for a number of years covering other ingredients known to cause problems with a minority of consumers, such as egg, wheatflour, garlic, soya, etc.

Similarly, although current legislation permits the use of various generic terms such as vegetable oil, we will always identify the presence of individual nut oils. Again, this is done either as a unique ingredient in its appropriate position or indicated as a component of the appropriate generic term.

These rules apply without exception and regardless of the level of nut derivative present; thus, we are particularly vigilant to declare even the presence of "carry- over" ingredients derived from, for example, groundnut oil used as a carrier for flavourings, spice oil, vitamins, etc. As indicated above, wherever possible we try to avoid the presence of these materials and, in practice, we find suppliers of these ingredients are generally responsive to a request to reformulate their materials without the nut derivatives.

In addition to our concerns for our customers and consumers, we have of course a clear responsibility towards our employees and any visitors to our various sites. At those sites where nut derivatives are handled, we therefore display prominent notices at the reception desks, alerting visitors who may be allergic to such materials that they should not enter the premises.

Our site staff restaurants have been issued with clear instructions on the use, handling and labelling of nut derivatives. In common with our product recipes, nut materials will only be used where their presence may reasonably be expected but, in all cases, their presence will be indicated at the counter. All nuts, nut oils and dishes containing nuts are handled with great care to prevent small amounts of cross-contamination.

We use specified oils such as sunflower and corn oil instead of generic vegetable oils or groundnut oil. No oils should be reused after they have been used for cooking nut-containing material or foodstuffs in order to avoid cross-contamination. In particular, restaurant staff are instructed to take great care when using leftovers to ensure that no subsequent dishes contain small amounts of nuts unexpectedly.

Clearly, it will take time for all necessary label changes to be implemented, even after all relevant HACCP studies have been carried out. As an interim measure, therefore (and totally mindful of the pitfalls to which reference will be made later in respect of databases), we also provide to individual consumers, on request, lists of our products that we can guarantee to be nut-free. However, in order to accommodate any subsequent manufacturing or other commercial changes, these lists carry a 6-month expiry date, clearly stating that the list is no longer valid after that time; upon expiry of the list, consumers are advised to contact the company for an updated list. If any changes are made to products within the currency of the lists, all consumers who have received a "nut-free" list during that 6-month period will be issued with an update. A telephone number is given should any consumers have any urgent enquiries.

All consumers who contact the Company regarding allergies are contacted personally by a company nutritionist and urged to discuss their problem with their GP or dietitian.

Although allergy to nuts and other foods is uncommon, we believe that the above procedures present a realistic and responsible approach to the problem. Although our policy has, historically, been focused on nuts, it is clearly applicable to other foods. However, as our knowledge and understanding of the issues improve, and as our product folio changes, we will be the first to realise that changes need to be made.

In particular, production rationalisation, international production and trading patterns, brand and range extensions all need to be considered on an ongoing basis; it may well be that greater prominence to our "may contain nut traces" statement will be required on certain products as the commercial situation develops.

Nestlé is essentially a branded house; our brands are our strength and many of them are household names, not only in the UK but also across the world. It is therefore legitimate and inevitable that these brands will be used for products in different food sectors; for example, we already have well known confectionery brands such as Aero and Rolo that are used, not only in the confectionery area, but also for milk-based drinks, dairy desserts and ice cream. These products are naturally produced in different locations, and the allergen status of each must be separately assessed. However, in the event that the parent brand, e.g. confectionery, is allergen-free whereas the range extension product may not be, serious consideration must be given to the mechanism for adequately alerting potential consumers, who may be fully aware of the safe status of the parent product, that the new introductions are not in the same category.

Similarly, a consumer in the UK may be fully aware that a product carries a "may contain nut traces" statement in the UK. The same consumer, travelling in Spain or France, may encounter ostensibly the same product but be totally unaware that it has been produced not only in a different factory but even in a different country, while carrying the same brand name. If the allergen status of the products in the UK and elsewhere in Europe were to be different, serious consideration would clearly need to be given to the prominence and adequacy of the labelling of the susceptible product. A further area that must be addressed by manufacturers is the change to a product status when the introduction of new products in the manufacturing environment might result in the potential for adventitious contamination. The handling of such a changeover, both via labelling and direct communication to the public at large, clearly needs to be considered in some detail before the introduction of such new products. Likewise, the change of production location of a "clean" product to another site, which might result in a risk of contamination, must be seriously considered; such changes in location might be driven either by production rationalisation or, indeed, short-term considerations.

LABELLING VERSUS DATABASES

The question has often been posed whether labelling of individual products is the appropriate route to follow or whether a more widespread use of food intolerance databases might offer a better solution. Such databases, covering those ingredients that are known to cause mild intolerance reactions, already exist in the UK and several other countries.

Whilst such databases may be of some value in the case of mild intolerances, they are not applicable to very serious allergens.

The basis upon which these national databases are constructed is not consistent between countries; some are based on 'free-from' listing; others contain only those products that should not be consumed (i.e. contain/may contain the potential allergen).

Our position on this issue is clear. There is only a very limited role, if any, for "free-from" databases in respect of potentially life-threatening allergens. The risks are too great to be handled on anything other than a day-to-day, specific product-by-product basis under the direct and absolute control of the company concerned. We see insuperable and commercially unacceptable risks arising from the need for individual consumers to be accurately advised of the suitability (or in reality unsuitability) of a given product to meet their needs at any given point in time.

We consider the concept of "free-from" life-threatening allergen databases operated by third parties to be fundamentally flawed, in that the data available to the public must be 100% accurate and reliable at all times. There is a paramount requirement to be able to accommodate the essential, commercial flexibility required by an international manufacturing and trading company such as Nestlé. It is quite unacceptable that, at short notice, we should be unable to import equivalent products from overseas or to transfer production between factories because the "free-from" status of the products is different.

Similarly, the introduction of a new variant of a long-established product may change the status of the latter; equally, the production of a new, nut-containing product alongside hitherto "clean" products may have fundamental implications for the status of existing products.

We do not believe that any third-party system can adequately address the types of product or production changes indicated above - and certainly not within a relevant timescale. It may, on occasion, be necessary to change the source of a product within a few days in the event of, say, strikes, raw material supply difficulties or other issues beyond local management control.

We do not believe that a database, particularly when organised on a national basis, will be capable of addressing the problems raised by ever-increasing international travel. For example, we have already experienced a problem with a consumer who had understood one of our brands to be wholly nut-free and was surprised to learn that a variant, imported from Italy was not. Equally, a well-known UK product may well be "nut-free" in the UK but the same product, manufactured in Germany and sold in France (labelled in all three languages for sale in, say, Euro Disney) may well not be.

The question of liability in the event of any adverse reactions being suffered by a consumer, based upon information obtained from databases in one country but inapplicable elsewhere, is an interesting one. As indicated earlier, Nestlé believes very clearly that it can only be the manufacturer who must take all the necessary steps to advise potential consumers on a case-by-case basis. The only safe and sure way of doing this is via the label of individual products, with the degree of prominence afforded to any allergen statements being determined by individual product circumstances.

3. THE US EXPERIENCE

Steve L. Taylor & Susan L. Hefle

Food allergies have been recognised in the US for many years. However, just as in the UK, the awareness of food allergies has increased in recent years. Until recently, the food industry, the medical community, and even individuals with food allergies displayed little concern, at least publicly, about food allergies. Now, there is increasing recognition of the prevalence and occasional severity of food allergies. Because of this increased awareness and concern, the US Food and Drug Administration (FDA) and the American food industry have begun to take actions to protect the allergic segment of the population.

Many reasons may exist for the increased awareness and concerns related to food allergies. For many years, the public's perception of food allergies has been skewed. Surveys have shown that 10-20% of the public believe that they or someone in their family has a food allergy.[1] The true prevalence of food allergies in the US is much lower, perhaps 1-2% of the population.[2,3,4] The symptoms associated with the falsely perceived food allergies are usually mild. In contrast, some of the individuals with true food allergies experience severe, life-threatening reactions. The public's perception is often that food allergies are mild, transitory adverse reactions that are more of a nuisance than a serious health concern. This false perception has led to a somewhat cavalier attitude about food allergies among a large segment of the population. This false perception has begun to disappear as awareness increases of the potential severity of true food allergies. Certainly, the US regulatory agencies and much of the American food industry are well aware of the true situation, although proper education of the entire population remains a challenge.

The attitude of the US FDA and the US food industry began to change with the publication of two key scientific papers. In 1988, Yunginger et al.[5] described eight deaths of food-allergic adults and teenagers associated with the inadvertent ingestion of the offending food. Several years later, Sampson et al.[6] described six deaths and six near-deaths occurring among food-allergic children and resulting from the inadvertent ingestion of the offending food. These publications convinced the US FDA that allergic reactions to certain foods could be fatal on occasion. As a direct result, the FDA has now established a policy that mandates Class I recalls of packaged foods found to contain unlabelled quantities of those allergenic foods that have been associated with known deaths.

Thus, packaged foods containing unlabelled peanuts, soya beans, eggs, shrimp, fish, etc., are subject to Class I recalls in the US. In Class I recalls, the responsible manufacturer is required to retrieve the mislabelled product from distribution warehouses, retail outlets, and homes. Press releases are typically required to alert the public to the existence of the mislabelled product. Furthermore, the FDA mandates Class II recalls for mislabelled, packaged foods that contain allergenic foods that are not known to have caused fatalities. Almonds, milk, and wheat would be examples of such foods. In Class II recalls, the responsible manufacturer must retrieve the product from distribution warehouses and retail outlets but not necessarily from homes. Press releases are often not required. Class III recalls can be mandated in certain, specialised situations with allergenic foods. If a packaged product, e.g. ice cream, is identified as containing peanuts, e.g. chocolate peanut butter ice cream, but the ingredient statement does not list peanuts, then the product could be subject to a Class III recall. In Class III recalls, the manufacturer is generally responsible only for retrieving products that are in his direct distribution channels and not from either retail outlets or homes.

The US food industry has become more aware of food allergies through the regulatory policies of the US FDA. In the US, there were no product recalls associated with the presence of unlabelled allergenic foods in packaged products in the early 1990s. That situation has changed dramatically. In 1996, over 50 recalls associated with unlabelled allergenic foods occurred in the US. Unlabelled allergenic foods are now one of the most common causes of food product recalls in the US and are certainly the fastest growing category of recalls. To our knowledge, all the food product recalls associated with unlabelled allergenic foods have been voluntary; they have been initiated by the manufacturers. Some of these recalls were initiated as the result of adverse reaction complaints often received by the companies and reported to the FDA. Many of the recalls have resulted from the increased vigilance of the food industry, who identified mislabelled products, informed the FDA, and acted to remove the products from the marketplace before receiving any consumer complaints. A few of the recalls, especially the Class III recalls, were initiated as a result of FDA inspections of processing facilities and products. This sizeable increase in the number of product recalls is testament to the increased awareness and concern of the US food industry regarding the potential severity of food allergies.

The public has become somewhat more aware of food allergies as a result of these product recalls. Class I recalls typically require press releases to inform the consuming public. The press releases are distributed in the area of the country where the implicated food product is sold. As a result, only a few of the press releases have been national in scope. Also, in the US, these recall notices are often not considered particularly newsworthy, probably because these illnesses affect only a small percentage of the population. Press coverage of these recall notices is patchy. In the print media, coverage is usually brief and is often found in sections of the newspapers that are not widely read. In contrast, press coverage is often extensive for foodborne illnesses that could affect anyone in the population, such as botulism or hepatitis. Thus, the majority of the consuming public are often unaware of a particular food allergy recall, and the recall mechanism is only partially effective in enhancing the awareness of the American public regarding the seriousness of food allergies.

Media coverage of specific allergic reactions to foods, even when the reactions are severe or fatal, is typically localised in the US. A food-allergy death will likely be covered by the local newspaper or television station. We are not aware of any instances where press coverage of severe reactions has been widespread in the US. However, it is our impression that food allergy deaths or severe reactions are much more likely to be recorded as such by the medical authorities. As a result, many news stories have appeared in a variety of communities in recent years leading to an enhanced awareness of food allergies and their severity among certain segments of the public. Last year, when several such episodes in the north-eastern US involved allergic reactions to peanuts, considerable negative publicity occurred in that region regarding peanuts. This publicity caused several school districts in that region to consider banning peanut products from schools. Curiously, little such publicity regarding peanuts occurred in other parts of the US at that time.

Another factor in increased public awareness of food allergies in the US has been the Food Allergy Network. The Food Allergy Network was created several years ago by the mother of a severely food-allergic child. The organisation has grown to more than 10,000 members. The Food Allergy Network publishes educational materials for food-allergic consumers and serves as an important and responsible contact for the media regarding food allergy information and quotations. The Food Allergy Network also serves as a route for notification of allergic consumers regarding product recall notices. The US food industry has begun to fund the mailing of recall notices to members of the Food Allergy Network. This serves as a very effective strategy for dissemination of this critical information to the affected segment of the population. The Food Allergy Network has also heightened the awareness of allergic individuals regarding the prevalence and severity of food allergies. Through its educational materials, the Food Allergy Network has increased the knowledge of allergic individuals regarding implementation of effective avoidance diets, industry labelling practices, and effective precautionary measures. The Food Allergy Network serves as a mechanism for effective communication within the allergy community (physicians, patients, parents) and between the allergic individuals and the food industry. As a result, the food industry is experiencing an increased number of calls for information on product composition and labelling terms. Also, as a result, the food industry is much more likely than in the past to learn about allergic reactions that might have occurred as a result of exposure to mislabelled products. This enhanced communication has resulted in improved industry awareness and contributed to the increase in product recalls and the implementation of improved industry quality assurance procedures with regard to allergenic foods.

The situation in Canada has also contributed to the increased awareness of food allergies in the US. Canadian authorities have taken the most proactive approach to food allergies of any government, in our view. Recalls of mislabelled products containing hazardous allergens began in

Canada several years before they occurred in the US. The Canadian authorities routinely inspect food-processing facilities for violations that might result in potentially hazardous residues of allergenic foods being present in other products. Severe allergic reactions to foods in Canada have received more widespread publicity than in the US, leading to a considerably greater degree of public awareness of the prevalence and severity of food allergies in Canada. With the considerable trade between the US and Canada, this heightened level of awareness of food allergies in Canada has spilled over into the US.

The prevalence of true food allergies in the US is often estimated at 1-2% of the population,[2,4] but is higher among infants than it is among adults.[3,4,7] The prevalence of true food allergies among infants in the US is 5-8%.[3,4] Obviously, therefore, many food-allergic infants outgrow their food allergies.[8,9] Only a small and unknown percentage of those with true food allergies experience severe, life-threatening reactions upon exposure to the offending food. There has been some concern in the US that the prevalence of true food allergies and especially the prevalence of severe food allergies might be increasing. Where no hard data exist to support this possibility, it may be true, and it has contributed to the increased concern among the public, the food industry, and government regulators.

The most common allergenic foods in the US are peanuts, milk, eggs, tree nuts (almonds, walnuts, hazelnuts, etc.), soya beans, fish (salmon, cod, etc.), crustacea (shrimp, crab, lobster), and wheat.[10] Among infants, milk, eggs, and peanuts are the most common allergenic foods,[3,11] but infants often outgrow their allergies to milk and eggs.[8,12] In contrast, few infants ever outgrow peanut allergy.[13] As a result, peanut allergy becomes the most common allergenic food among adults in the US. The crustacea are probably the second most common allergenic food among American adults, although good data on the prevalence of specific types of food allergies in US adults do not exist. Most of the regulatory attention in the US is aimed at the eight foods or food groups listed above. It has been estimated that these eight foods or food groups account for 90% of all food allergies in the US.[10]

Many other foods are associated less commonly with food allergies.[10] A few of these foods are recognised to cause severe allergic reactions on occasion. Sesame seeds, poppy seeds, cottonseed, sunflowerseed, certain other legumes (lentils, garbanzo beans, etc.), and molluscan shellfish (oysters, clams, etc.) would fall into this category.

The eight foods or food groups listed above are also recognised as the most commonly allergenic foods on a worldwide basis.[14] Some geographical differences do exist in the prevalence of specific food allergies. At one time, peanut allergy was probably more common in North America than in the rest of the world because of its affection for peanut butter. However, worldwide consumption of peanuts has increased with a resultant, almost predictable, increase in the prevalence of peanut allergy on a worldwide basis. Celery allergy, which is common in Europe,[15] is uncommon in the US for reasons that are not known. The prevalence of tree nut allergies, while not thoroughly studied, probably varies between the UK and the US. Hazelnut allergy is common in Europe,[16] probably because Europeans are quite fond of hazelnuts and because hazelnuts are cross-reactive with birch pollen, a common pollen allergy in Europe. Hazelnut allergy seems less common in the US. Brazil nut allergy is common in the UK[17] because of the popularity of Brazil nut confections, but seems less common in the US. In contrast, almond, walnut, and pecan allergies appear to be the most common of the tree nut allergies in the US because these particular tree nuts are widely consumed by Americans.

The symptoms of true food allergies in the US are diverse and involve the gastrointestinal tract (nausea, vomiting, diarrhoea), the skin (urticaria, angioedema, dermatitis), and the respiratory tract (rhinitis, asthma).[17] The most alarming symptom associated with allergic reactions to foods is anaphylactic shock, a severe systemic reaction involving the gastrointestinal tract, the skin, the respiratory tract, and the cardiovascular tract. Anaphylactic shock can result in death within a few minutes of onset. Fortunately, only a small percentage of individuals with food allergies experience such severe reactions upon exposure to specific allergenic foods. None of the public health agencies in the US maintains records on the numbers of deaths or severe reactions associated with allergic reactions to foods in this country. However, estimates have been made that perhaps as many as 950 severe reactions occur per year in the US as the result of food allergies.[18] In studies of deaths or severe reactions associated with food allergies, peanuts and tree nuts are the most commonly implicated foods;[5,6] however, fish, crustacea, soya beans, milk, and eggs have been associated with deaths as well. The individuals involved in these deaths can be either children or adults, although teenagers seem to be the most vulnerable group. The individuals are aware of their food allergies and are often aware of the potential severity of their reactions. Asthma, while not a common symptom in food allergies, is often a complicating factor among individuals experiencing severe reactions.[6] In these cases, exposure usually occurs away from home, often in food-service establishments, as the result of inadvertent ingestion of the offending foods. Frequently, in cases that result in death, no medication is immediately available to treat the allergic reaction. Although some of these patients have been prescribed epinephrine, they do not always carry this critical medication with them. Epinephrine is widely recognised as a life-saving antidote for severe, food-allergic reactions.[6]

Food-allergic individuals typically avoid adverse reactions by implementation of specific avoidance diets.[19] However, the degree of tolerance for the offending food is often quite low, probably milligram amounts.[20] As a result, these individuals are vulnerable to ingestion of mere traces of the offending food. In the US, it is increasingly recognised that certain practices in the food-service and food-processing industries can lead to the potential presence of hazardous allergenic residues.

In food-service establishments, the sharing of utensils, containers, or cooking/preparation surfaces can lead to cross-contamination. The ingestion of french-fried potatoes that were fried in the same oil used for the deep-fat frying of fish probably caused the fatal reaction of one fish-allergic individual.[5] The lack of labelling for foods in restaurants is another factor. When that factor is coupled with an uninformed waiting or cooking staff, the results can be devastating. Creative recipe formulation in restaurants occasionally contributes to adverse reactions. The use of peanut butter in the formulation for chili in a restaurant probably caused the death of a peanut-allergic teenager.[5]

In food-processing facilities, the use of shared equipment is a major factor in cross-contamination. The use of dairy-processing equipment for the manufacture of sorbet or soya-based frozen dessert (tofutti) resulted in the contamination of these products with milk residues that led to allergic reactions.[21,22] Similarly, the use of peanut butter processing equipment for the manufacture of a novel sunflower butter product resulted in peanut contamination of the sunflower butter product and several allergic reactions.[23] The use of re-work, the food industry's leftovers, can also contribute to cross-contamination and allergic reactions.[24,25] The switching of ingredients has the potential to confuse consumers and contribute to allergic reactions. In one such incident, the manufacturer of hot dogs changed the natural flavouring in its hot dogs from autolysed yeast to hydrolysed casein. Casein is one of the major allergens in milk, and the hydrolysis process was not sufficient to remove the allergenicity of this ingredient. As a result, several milk-allergic consumers became ill from eating these hot dogs.[22] Mix-ups in packaging can result in obvious problems, and, labelling terms can often be confusing to consumers. In the hot dog incident described above, consumers would have no way of knowing that "natural flavoring" could signify the presence of milk.

The food industry can do much to control allergic reactions to their products. We advocate the use of a HACCP-like (Hazard Analysis Critical Control Point) strategy. The industry can take actions to control the presence of undeclared quantities of allergenic foods in its products, and it can also take action to alert consumers to the presence of allergenic foods in its products through labelling.

Labelling is considered the key to the control of food-allergic reactions to packaged foods by the food industry, the government regulators, and allergic consumers in the US. Fortunately, the US and Canada have perhaps the most comprehensive labelling regulations in the world. US regulations mandate that virtually all the ingredients present in foods be declared on the label. Certain ingredients can be listed collectively, such as natural flavours, artificial flavours, and spices. However, with a few exceptions, such as the hot dog incident noted above, these collective terms do not cause problems. Processing aids, substances that are used during the processing of a food but which have no functional effect in the finished product and which are present at low levels in the finished product, also need not be declared on the ingredient statement. However, the FDA has recently informed manufacturers that residual materials that could cause allergic reactions cannot be considered to be processing aids. We advocate that the industry should always declare the presence of any commonly allergenic food (milk, eggs, peanuts, soya beans, fish, crustacea, tree nuts, and wheat) on the ingredients list if the product is known to contain such ingredients. The sources of ingredients should be declared when the ingredients are derived from allergenic sources. An example would be 'hydrolysed peanut protein'. Also, the source of flavouring materials should be declared if the flavouring formulation contains proteins from known allergenic sources, e.g. "natural flavouring (contains milk)".

The US food industry has become much more proactive in alerting consumers to the presence of allergenic ingredients. Most companies have always endeavoured to declare the presence of allergenic foods on the ingredients statement, in part because it is required by regulation in the US. Companies are beginning to identify the sources of ingredients where that might not be clear to all consumers. Consumers must still know that casein and whey are synonymous with milk. But companies are increasingly using labelling terms such as 'natural flavoring (contains milk)' to assist allergic consumers. As an additional aid, one US company is highlighting allergenic components in bold print on ingredients labels. 'May contain' labelling is not specifically allowed in the US, although it is in Canada. In Canada, 'may contain' labelling is allowed in situations where contamination is documented, uncontrollable, sporadic, and potentially hazardous, a very reasonable position that we endorse. A few US companies are using 'may contain' labelling in similar situations, and the FDA has taken no action against them. However, 'may contain' labelling should never be used as a substitute for Good Manufacturing Practices, including effective clean-up procedures. Several US companies list one or more allergenic foods at the end of the ingredients list if residues of these foods routinely exist in the product as the result of the use of shared equipment.

In product development, the food industry can take certain actions with respect to allergenic foods. When formulating new food products, commonly allergenic foods and ingredients derived from these foods should be avoided whenever possible. Certainly, commonly allergenic food ingredients should not be used if other ingredients will function equally as well. The use of allergenic ingredients in such small amounts that they have no functional effect in the finished product should be avoided. Where possible, ingredients used should be those that are already present in other products manufactured on the same equipment; this will decrease the amount of attention that must be paid to clean-up between products (see below). Caution should always be exercised in the reformulation of existing food products. If allergenic ingredients are newly introduced to the product, special steps should be taken to alert allergic individuals to the presence of such new ingredients. If commonly allergenic foods or ingredients derived from these foods are used, precautions must be taken to be sure that these ingredients are always readily identifiable on product labels. In the case of ingredients derived from allergenic foods, an assessment of the protein content of the ingredient will indicate if this ingredient should be identified by source on the package label.

The major ingredient questions involve edible oils, hydrolysed proteins, lecithin, and flavours. Edible oils are safe for consumption by allergic individuals if they are refined, bleached, and deodorised. Such oils contain no protein residues, and thus no allergens. Highly refined peanut oil, soyabean oil, and sunflowerseed oils have been documented to be safe for allergic consumers.[26,27,28,29] Hydrolysed proteins must be declared by source in the US. Although extensively hydrolysed proteins may be safe for allergic consumers, such ingredients in commerce vary rather widely in their degrees of hydrolysis. Since hydrolysed proteins are often derived from commonly allergenic foods, including peanuts, soya beans, and wheat, declaration of the source on the label seems prudent. Lecithin is primarily derived from soya beans and eggs, which are both commonly allergenic foods. While lecithin from soya beans is known to contain protein residues, its allergenicity has not been established. Some allergists do not advocate its avoidance by soya-bean-allergic individuals while others do. It is not required in the US that the source of the lecithin be declared on the label, although soya-bean lecithin is used much more frequently than egg lecithin. In the US, flavours can be collectively declared as either artificial flavours or natural flavours. There is no requirement for the identification of any particular flavouring ingredients. However, as indicated earlier, some manufacturers are voluntarily identifying the presence of flavourings derived from allergenic sources in instances where that occurs.

Many US food companies have also begun to adopt improved manufacturing practices, which decrease the likelihood of cross-contamination. Shared equipment and facilities are commonly used in the food industry. Thorough clean-up of shared equipment is routinely conducted between products containing an allergenic ingredient and products that do not contain such an ingredient. Companies often schedule the manufacturing of highly allergenic products just before the end of major production cycles so that major clean-up of the equipment can be conducted. Some companies have chosen to isolate specific allergenic products to one or a few manufacturing locations. Another strategy involves scheduling long runs of allergenic products on the equipment so that changeovers and clean-up are minimised. Also, the allergenic components should be introduced into the product as late as possible in the process so that the area for clean-up is minimised. The separation of processing lines, packaging lines, and personnel is certainly a useful strategy when it can be employed. One confectionery manufacturer has transferred processing of peanut-containing products mostly to one specific plant and moved all of the company's products that do not contain peanuts to other manufacturing sites. To avoid costly clean-ups of multiple facilities, it may be wise to consider moving all manufacturing of particularly allergenic products, such as those containing peanuts, to one location. US companies are increasingly dedicating processing and/or packaging lines to specific allergenic products. Processing operations have been carefully inspected to ensure that product flows do not allow unexpected cross-contamination. Allergenic ingredients should be stored in specific areas in well-marked containers to avoid mix-ups. In-process totes should be clearly labelled so that those containing allergenic components are readily identifiable. Re-work policies have been restricted to 'like-into-like' by many US companies.

While adoption of these practices is still not uniform, the US food industry is making great strides in the recognition and control of allergens in foods. With sensible strategies, such as those described above, the food industry can dramatically decrease the likelihood that unlabelled allergenic ingredients will be present in packaged food products.

REFERENCES

1. A perspective on popular perceptions of adverse reactions to foods.
    Sloan AE & Powers ME
    J. Allergy Clin. Immunol. (1986) 78:127.

2. Allergic reactions to foods.
    Anderson JA.
    Crit. Rev. Food Sci. Nutr. (1996) 36:S19-S38.

3. Patterns of food hypersensitivity during sixteen years of double-blind, placebo-controlled food challenges.
    Bock SA & Atkins FM
    J. Pediatr. (1990) 117:561.

4. Food allergy.
    Sampson HA
    Curr. Opinion Immunol. (1990) 2:542.

5. Fatal food-induced anaphylaxis.
    Yunginger J W, Sweeney KG, Sturner WQ, Giannandrea LA, Teigland JD,
    Bray M, Benson PA, York JA, Biedrzycki L, Squillace DL & Helm RM
    J. Am. Med. Assoc. (1988) 260:1450.

6. Fatal and near-fatal food-induced anaphylaxis in children.
    Sampson HA, Mendelson L, & Rosen JP
    N. Engl. J. Med. (1992) 327:380.

7. Allergic reactions and food intolerances.
    Lemke PJ & Taylor SL
    In: Nutritional Toxicology. Eds FN Kotsonis, M Mackey, & J Hjelle
    Raven Press, New York, (1994) pp. 117.

8. The natural history of food sensitivity.
    Bock SA
    J. Allergy Clin. Immunol. (1982) 69:173.

9. Natural history of cow milk allergy: clinical outcome.
    Bishop JM, Hill DJ & Hosking CS
    J. Pediatr. (1990) 116:862.

10. Allergenic foods.
    Hefle SL, Nordlee JA & Taylor SL
    Crit. Rev. Food Sci. Nutr. (1996) 36:S69-S89.

11. Food hypersensitivity and atopic dermatitis: evaluation of 113 patients.
    Sampson HA & McCaskill CC
    J. Pediatr. (1985) 107:669.

12. Natural history of food hypersensitivity in children with atopic dermatitis.
    Sampson HA & Scanlon SM
    J. Pediatr. (1989) 115:23.

13. The natural history of peanut allergy.
    Bock SA & Atkins FM
    J. Allergy Clin. Immunol. (1989) 83:900.

14. Report of the FAO Technical Consultation on Food Allergies.
    Food and Agriculture Organization of the United Nations
    Rome, Italy, November 13 to 14, 1995.

15.   Celery allergy associated with birch and mugwort pollinosis.
      Wuthrich B, Stager J & Johannson S
      Allergy (1990) 45:566.

16.   Identification of common allergenic structures in hazel pollen and
      hazelnuts: a possible explanation for sensitivity to hazelnuts in patients
      allergic to tree pollen.
      Hirschwehr R, Valenta R, Ebner C, Ferreira F, Sperr WR, Valent P, Rohac
      M, Rumpold H, Scheiner D & Kraft D
      J. Allergy Clin. Immunol. (1992) 90:927.

17.   Clinical and immunological characteristics of Brazil nut allergy.
      Arshad SH, Malmberg E, Krapt K & Hide DW
      Clin. Exp. Allergy (1991) 21:373.

18.   The incidence of severe adverse reactions to food in Colorado.
      Bock SA
      J. Allergy Clin. Immunol. (1992) 90:683.

19.   Avoidance diets - how selective should we be?
      Taylor SL, Bush RK & Busse WW
      N. Engl. Reg. Allergy Proc. (1986) 7:527.

20.   Principles and characteristics of food allergens.
      Taylor SL & Lehrer SB
      Crit. Rev. Food Sci. Nutr. (1996) 36:S91-S118.

21.   Anaphylaxis in a milk-allergic child after ingestion of milk-contaminated
      kosher-pareve-labeled "dairy-free" dessert.
      Jones RT, Squillace DL & Yunginger JW
      Ann. Allergy (1992) 68:223.

22.   Allergic reactions to milk-contaminated "nondairy" products.
      Gern JE, Yang E, Evrard HM & Sampson HA
      N. Engl. J. Med. (1991) 324:976.

23.   Use of radioimmunoassay to determine the nature, quantity and source of
      allergenic contamination of sunflower butter.
      Yunginger JW, Gauerke MB, Jones RT, Dahlberg MJE & Ackerman S J
      J. Food Protection (1983) 46:625.

24.   Anaphylaxis from undeclared walnut in commercially processed cookies.
      Nordlee JA, Atkins FM, Bush RK & Taylor SL
      J. Allergy Clin. Immunol. (1993) 91 (Abstr.):154.

25.   Peanut anaphylaxis from food cross-contamination.
       Kemp SF & Lockey RF
       J. Am. Med. Assoc. (1996) 275:1636.

26.   Soybean oil is not allergenic to soybean-sensitive individuals.
       Bush RK, Taylor SL, Nordlee JA & Busse WW
       J. Allergy Clin. Immunol. (1985) 76:242-5.

27.   Sunflower oil is not allergenic to sunflower seed-sensitive patients.
       Halsey AB, Martin ME, Ruff ME, Jacobs FO & Jacobs RL
       J. Allergy Clin. Immunol. (1986) 78:408-10.

28.   Randomised, double blind, crossover challenge study of allergenicity of
       peanut oils in subjects allergic to peanuts.
       Hourihane JO, Bedwani SJ, Dean TP & Warner JO
       Br. Med. J. (1997) 314:1084-8.

29.   Peanut oil is not allergenic to peanut-sensitive individuals.
       Taylor SL, Busse WW, Sachs MI, Parker JL & Yunginger JW
       J. Allergy Clin. Immunol. (1981) 68:372-5.

4. PEANUT ALLERGY AND THE PEANUT OIL DEBATE

Jonathan O'B Hourihane

BACKGROUND

The incidence and prevalence of atopy and asthma have increased in the developed world over the last three decades.[1,2] Hospital admissions for asthma have increased[3] and recent anecdotal reports suggest an increase in referrals for evaluation of food allergy. Changes in ascertainment and case definition do not account for these changes, although they undoubtedly contribute to the apparent increase.[4,5]

It is apparent that, despite the general increase in allergy and atopy over the last 30 years, the issue of peanut allergy has received very little attention until recently. In contrast, from 1993 to 1996, the words peanut and allergy appear in the title or abstract of 44 original papers identified by a computer-based literature search.

A certain J H Kellog of Battle Creek, Michigan, was granted a patent in 1897 for the manufacture of "nut butter" and "nut meal" (US Patent 580,787).[6] Peanuts and peanut-containing foods now constitute a major part of the American diet. Americans eat between 2.9 and 3.6 kg of peanut products per person per year (data of National Peanut Council of America - NPCA).[7]

America produces 2 million tonnes of peanut per annum (only 10% of annual global peanut production) but accounts for 38% of exported peanuts. Seventy per cent of US exports are to Europe, largely via Britain and Holland. Britain imported 101,836 tonnes of unprocessed peanuts in 1994.

The value to the US economy of peanut as a cash crop is $1 billion (American billions) per annum. This is solely for peanut as used for nuts and baking (36% of production) and butter (50%), excluding oil (approximately 14%, Fig. 4.1), so the real figure is somewhat higher. This minimum figure for peanut is dwarfed by the impact of corn for human use, $23 billion a year, and wheat, $8 billion a year.

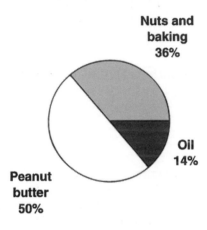

Total production: 2m metric tons pa
Data from National Peanut Council of America

Fig. 4.1 Food uses of peanut in USA

Peanut and peanut butter only appeared in significant quantities in Europe following the arrival of American troops in massive numbers, after 1942. Increasing Americanisation of lifestyle and diet have caused peanut and peanut products to become established as an important part of the snack diet of both adults (usually as dried or roasted kernels) and especially children (usually as peanut butter). The average British consumption per capita in 1994 was 1.77 kg (NPCA).

EXPOSURE AND SENSITISATION TO PEANUT EARLY IN LIFE

Evidence of early sensitisation to peanut is presented in Table 4.I.

TABLE 4.I
Evidence of early sensitisation to peanut

		Reference
General	Food-reactive T cells in blood of newborn infants	Warner[11] Szepfalusi[12]
	Food protein-specific IgE found in blood of newborn infants before post-natal exposure	Host[10]
	All American children exposed to peanut by 2 years	Zeiger[15]
Specific	Age of onset of peanut allergy is apparently decreasing	Hourihane[8] Ewan[16]
	Recent increase of consumption of peanut by pregnant and nursing mothers	Hourihane[8]
	4/54 newborn infants (<11 days) showed positive skin prick test with peanut	Hatahet[9]
	Peanut protein retrievable from breast milk	De Bolt[13]
	Babies may react clinically to peanut in breast milk	Hourihane (unpublished)
	80% of peanut allergics react to first obvious exposure to peanut	Hourihane[14]
	0.6% of 4-year-olds are peanut allergic and another 0.7% have positive sensitivity tests	Tariq[29]

Seventy-five per cent of peanut allergic subjects have an atopic parent, although less than 2% have a parent with peanut allergy (Table 4.II).[8] This suggests that, as in other allergies, the predisposition to allergy is inherited, in a polygenic rather than a single gene mode, and that peanut allergy is a manifestation of atopy which is provoked by peanut exposure in a genetically predisposed child.

The role of interplay of genetic predisposition to allergy and exposure to antigen is further emphasised by the virtual absence of peanut allergy in populations such as those of subequatorial Africa, which have low rates of all forms of atopy but high rates of consumption of peanut. Crushed peanuts are often introduced to the diet of Korean children from weaning at approximately 6 months, but peanut allergy is almost unknown in Korea (KS Park, personal communication).

TABLE 4.II
Atopy in parents of 595 British peanut allergics*

Atopic parent	Number	%
Either parent atopic	447	75
Only mother atopic	174	29
Only father atopic	119	20
Both parents atopic	154	26
Neither parent atopic	148	25

* There were 605 parental pairs. Data were incomplete for 10 subjects and unavailable for a further 17 individuals   Adapted from Hourihane[8]

Hatahet skin-tested (by the skin prick test method) 54 newborn infants (less than 11 days) and 71 babies aged between 17 days and 4 months old.[9] Eight per cent of both groups had positive skin tests to peanut, implying sensitisation (or priming of a potentially allergic reaction) in the womb or soon after birth. The antibody responsible for most immediate allergic reactions, IgE, does not traverse the placenta; therefore, if IgE is detected in a foetus or newborn baby, it has been produced by the baby. Proteins and fragments of proteins other than peanut have been shown to be capable of causing foetal production of IgE,[10] and newborn (cord) blood T cells to be reactive to specific antigens.[11,12]

Peanut antigens are also retrievable from breast milk. De Bolt studied nine nursing mothers who excluded legumes from their diets for 24 hours, before eating 90 g of roasted peanuts. Peak peanut allergen levels in breast milk occurred at varying times, varying from 1 hour to 5 hours.[13] We know of one child who reacted, from the age of 3-4 months, to breast feeds after the mother ate peanuts. Her reactions consisted of loose offensive stools, crying and irritability, starting within 30 minutes of the feed, lasting for 24 hours. She was clinically sensitive to egg taken orally after weaning from the breast, which caused perioral urticaria but her mother had not associated any symptoms to breast feeds after she had eaten egg herself. At 11 months the baby had positive reactions on skin prick test with egg (7 mm), milk (5 mm) and peanut (3 mm). She remains on a diet free of egg and peanut, but containing milk. A peanut challenge will be considered in the future. We have shown a recent increase in peanut consumption by pregnant and breast-feeding mothers whose children have later been shown to be peanut-allergic.[8]

In the group of 622 people who reported peanut allergy and participated in our questionnaire survey, 501 (81%) said they had reacted to their first obvious exposure to peanut.[14] The frequency of consumption of peanut early in life was demonstrated by Zeiger's study of the role of allergen avoidance in infancy in the prevention of allergy. The study identified 410 pregnant mothers whose unborn child was considered at high risk of developing allergic illnesses after birth. Before birth, 103 mothers were randomised to a diet that excluded milk, eggs, and peanut in the last trimester of pregnancy and while breast feeding (the prophylactically treated group). The mothers were required to delay introduction of egg, peanut and fish to the infants' diets for 12 months. One hundred and eighty-five infants were randomised to normal maternal diet and standard weaning diets (control group). At 12 months, asthma, eczema and food allergy were less common in the prophylactically treated group (16.2%) than in the control group (27%, p=0.04). Nearly 60% of the control group (unrestricted diet) had eaten peanut before their first birthday, compared with 18% of the prophylactically treated group, who were meant to be avoiding peanut.[15] This high rate of consumption in both Zeiger's groups may differ from British dietary practice, owing to the ubiquity of peanut butter in the American diet, but in general the two countries' diets are becoming more similar. Peanut butter has become a common snack food for children in Britain.

In a recent British report of 24 nut allergics who presented under the age of two, 23 reactions were due to peanuts. Peanut accounted for all cases who were allergic to a nut by the age of one year. It was concluded that sensitisation to peanuts or nuts had occurred at an early age - "considerably earlier than the age at presentation".[16]

After dealing with a case of anaphylaxis in which the only potential source of allergen was peanut oil, De Montis showed that a positive skin prick test with peanut was demonstrable in 22/112 (20%) of children referred to an allergy clinic. The reason for referral was not specified. Two of the cases were in a group of 40 children who had received vitamin D preparations that did not contain peanut oil, compared with 20/72 (28%) children whose vitamin D preparations did contain peanut oil.[17] It must be pointed out that details were not available for the prevalence of peanut allergy (as opposed to skin test positivity) or for exposure to peanuts in the children's diets in either group.

Moneret-Vautrin has identified peanut oil in infant formulae as a source of allergen, causing eczema and also acute oral reactions in four infants.[18] A skin prick test with peanut was positive in each child and positive with peanut oil in the single child tested. Withdrawal of milk formulas containing peanut oils from these children's diets caused improvement of their eczema, which worsened on challenge. From this report it cannot be certain that the oils were responsible for the sensitisation because no information is given about maternal diet while the mother was pregnant or breast feeding. Oral challenge with the oil did, however, show that the oil caused urticarial reactions in all four cases.

In contrast to these findings, a third French group failed to sensitise guinea pigs with peanut oil given by mouth. A control group of guinea pigs was successfully sensitised with peanuts given orally, and the blood of these animals could be used to transfer sensitivity to other guinea pigs (passive cutaneous anaphylaxis), whereas the blood of the animals fed peanut oil had no effect.[19] Even crude oil has a low protein concentration, however, and concern has recently been expressed again regarding the role in sensitisation of skin preparations containing peanut oil.[20,21,22] There have been no studies of the allergenicity of topically applied peanut oil and it could be a fruitful area of research. In the absence of data, several cosmetics manufacturers have chosen to remove peanut oils from their formulations.[23,24]

PREVALENCE OF PEANUT ALLERGY, ESPECIALLY IN CHILDREN

Food allergy affects up to 8% of pre-school children[25] and between 1 and 2% of adults.[26,27] Bock & Sampson[28] found that 93% of positive double-blind, placebo-controlled food challenges (DBPCFCs) in children are caused by just eight foods - in order of frequency - egg, peanut, milk, soya, tree nuts, crustacean shellfish (not mollusc), fish and wheat. In a cohort study of 4-year-old children on the Isle of Wight, 13/981 children (1.3%) were reactive on skin testing with peanut, although only 6/13 had actually had an allergic reaction to peanut.[29] It is uncertain how many of the other seven children with a positive peanut skin test will turn out to be allergic rather than merely sensitised in a non-clinical sense. The prevalence of peanut allergy in the general population is certainly lower than 1.3%, because not all age groups have been exposed to peanut as much as children born in the last 10 years,[8] when all forms of atopy have become more common.

PERSISTENCE OF PEANUT ALLERGY

Peanut allergy is considered to be a life-long problem. Considering its early onset and clinical severity (discussed below), the diagnosis is extremely distressing and disappointing for affected families, in contrast to the other common allergies of childhood - milk and egg - which usually remit. Twenty-five per cent of the Southampton group of peanut allergics reported having had a reaction in the 6 months before enrolment, and, in total, 50% in the previous year.[14] This supports the results of the most widely quoted study in this area.[30] Bock & Atkins reported the results of a follow-up study of a group of 32 children who had positive DBPCFCs with peanut. Many had suffered frequent accidental reactions (16/32 in the previous year). Skin prick tests were positive 2-10 years after the original positive skin test. One patient had a reaction 11 years after the positive DBPCFC. The authors conclude from this study that peanut allergy is rarely outgrown: "No children in this group who were exposed to peanuts by ingestion have been able to tolerate peanuts 2-14 years after an unequivocal diagnosis with double-blind food challenge".

More recently, the same group published, in abstract form, interim findings of an ongoing study of younger children.[31] They have been following 60 children under the age of 4 years. Forty-five per cent of these children have suffered a reaction 1-5 years after the diagnosis. No child has outgrown peanut allergy. There has been one near-death reaction. The findings of these two studies suggest that peanut allergy is persistent, and frequent accidental exposure is the rule rather than the exception.

SEVERITY OF ALLERGIC REACTIONS TO PEANUT

Foods cause severe allergic or anaphylactic reactions in between 1 in 90,000[32,33] and 1 in 264,000 people per year.[34] Yunginger[35] and Sampson[36] showed the most common causes of food-related anaphylactic reactions (some fatal) in adults and older children to be peanuts, crustacean shellfish, tree nuts and fish. Peanut can account for up to a third of all severe food-related allergic reactions.[34]

The severe nature of peanut allergy is emphasised further by the fact that a double-blind challenge test to prove peanut allergy is usually either unnecessary, owing to the classic history, or precluded by the severe nature of the reaction. In Denver, Colorado, one of the American centres doing food challenges most frequently, nearly half of peanut-allergic patients were not challenged, owing to the severe nature of the reported reaction. This exclusion of half the patients (18 out of 34) contrasts with 5 out of 90 egg-allergic patients and 3 out of 32 milk-allergic patients.[28]

In our clinical practice, severe allergic reactions are defined by the presence of wheeze or low blood pressure. Mild reactions consist of local itching and urticaria (nettle rash). Moderate reactions are those that comprise facial swelling, more generalised swelling or urticaria and throat tightness (which needs to be distinguished from wheezing, which implies narrowing of the bronchi). Other groups consider throat tightness a severe symptom.[16] It is an alarming feature of peanut allergy in Britain that, in our survey of 622 peanut allergic subjects, 40% of first reactions included wheezing, thereby immediately identifying the subject as severely allergic. A further 40-50% of subjects had other severe or moderate symptoms, leaving only 10-20% of subjects classifiable as mildly allergic after the first reaction.[14]

It is not an automatic assumption that each successive reaction is always worse than the preceding one. A dose effect is clearly evident, with most subjects who are challenged under supervision in hospital having lesser symptoms than they reported previously Table 4.III.[37] The risk of severe reactions is reduced by the practice of starting challenges with low doses. Doses are only increased, after set periods of observation, if no reaction is observed. The challenge is carefully administered to eliminate complicating factors (Table 4.IV) such as the understandable anxiety brought on by an unexpected exposure to peanut in restaurants and prepared meals, when remote from medical help.

TABLE 4.III
Positive peanut challenges in 56 subjects*

Dose of peanut (approximate dose of peanut protein)	Mild reaction Number	Moderate reaction Number	Severe reaction Number	Total Number
Labial[a]	35	4	1	40
Half nut (80 mg)	8	4	-	12
4 nuts (645 mg)	2	-	-	2
16 nuts (2.58 g)	2	-	-	2
Total	47	8	1	56

* 4 subjects who reacted to crude oil were not challeged with peanut
[a] Labial challenge required the cut edge of a peanut kernel being rubbed 10 times on the left side of the lower lip
Adapted from Hourihane[37]

TABLE 4.IV
Factors that aggravate allergic reactions to foods

Factor pre-dating food exposure   **Reference**

Cardiovascular disease

Asthma   Sampson[36]
                                                                        Hourihane[14]

Regular medication beta-blockers,   Hepner[38]
ACE inhibitors   Hermann[39]

Recent exercise   Tilles[40]

Occurring at or close to food exposure

Eating away from subject's home   Yunginger[35]
                                                                        Sampson[36]

Large does of allergenic food
Consumption of alcohol with food   Yunginger[35]

Anxiety caused by reaction (and by   Hourihane[37]
lack of trained assistance)

Delay of self medication (adrenaline)   Yunginger[35]
                                                                        Sampson[36]

Occurring after food exposure

Delay in seeking help   Yunginger[35]
                                                                        Sampson[36]

CROSS-REACTIVITY WITH LEGUMES

Until recently, there has been broad advice that food-allergic individuals should avoid related foods in case of cross-reactivity. Allergenic cross-reactivity has been shown between inhalant and food allergens[41,42] and also between pistachio and other members of the anacardiacae family, mangos and cashews.[43,44]

Peanut is a legume, not a nut. In vitro studies of peanut have shown extensive cross-reactivity with other legumes. Barnett showed that there was extensive reactivity between the serum of peanut-allergic peanuts and 11 different legumes.[45] However, clinical studies suggest that the evidence of significant in vivo reactivity to legumes in peanut allergics is weak.[30]

The first extensively investigated major peanut allergen was designated Ara h I (from the Latin name for peanut, Arachis hypogea).[46,47] Ara h I has been shown to be a vicillin protein, sharing important sequence identities with proteins of soya,[48] but the same group of workers showed that the areas of homology between peanut and soya-bean vicillins were not those that significantly bound IgE.[49]

Only 6% of British peanut allergics surveyed by our group reported soya allergy. In a subgroup of 43 peanut-allergic children, only 1 (2.3%) reported soya allergy and was skin test positive to soya. Four others (10%) were skin test positive to soya but not soya-allergic. Only 3 subjects (7%) were skin test positive to common pea.[8]

CROSS-REACTIVITY WITH TREE NUTS OR COINCIDENT PEANUT AND TREE NUT ALLERGY?

Cross-reactivity with tree nuts would be unexpected on the basis of the taxonomic disparity between peanuts and tree nuts, but clinical reactivity to tree nuts is a significant problem for peanut-allergics. It is uncertain whether this is due to coincident allergy or genuine cross-reactivity. Walnut and brazil nuts have similar storage proteins, and one walnut protein is 46% homologous with the major brazil nut antigen 2S albumin.[50] The 2S protein is rich in methionine, in which soya is relatively poor and transfer of this 2S albumin to transgenic soya beans also transfers allergenicity. Transgenic soya beans, containing the brazil 2S protein, inhibited the binding of brazil-specific IgE and caused positive skin prick tests in brazil-allergics.[51] Five of 12 British people who were allergic to brazil nut were also allergic to peanut[52] and only 28 of 47 peanut allergic people (mostly children) were allergic only to peanuts.[16]

In our group of 622 subjects who were studied using a questionnaire, 308 (49.5%) reported allergy to tree nuts. Forty-three children who had positive histories of peanut allergy and positive peanut skin test results were also evaluated for tree nut allergy. Nine (21%) reported tree nut allergy but only five of the nine had a positive skin test to any tree nut. Of the 34 subjects (79%) who did not report tree-nut allergy, nine had a positive skin test to a tree nut. Skin tests with tree nut solutions, therefore, have little diagnostic value in peanut-allergic children.[8]

In a subgroup of 60 peanut-allergic adults who attended for peanut and peanut-oil challenges,[37] 40 (66%) reported a history (Hx) of allergy to one or more tree nuts, but 50 (83%) had a positive skin test to one or more tree nuts (Fig. 4.2). In all peanut-allergic subjects who had skin tests with tree nut, the test was 69% sensitive and 65% specific for clinical sensitisation (unpublished data).

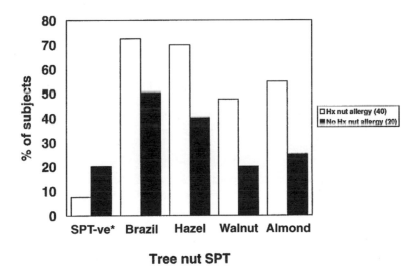

Fig. 4.2 Tree nut SPT in 60 peanut allergic adults

The relative frequency of reported allergy to individual tree nuts in peanut-allergic individuals suggests that allergy to a tree nut occurs in a similar frequency to their rates of consumption by the population, with reactions to almond, hazel and brazil being far more common than reactions to pecan, pistachio and cashew. Further studies must be undertaken to establish whether peanut and tree nut allergy develop separately or whether peanuts and tree nuts share allergenic protein sequences which cross-react.

ACCIDENTAL EXPOSURE TO HIDDEN PEANUT ANTIGENS IN PREPARED FOODS

Peanut is widely used and there is very poor awareness of its potentially lethal effects in tiny doses. People who are allergic to peanuts avoid peanuts stringently, and apart from deliberate challenge studies under medical supervision, subsequent reactions are the results of accidental exposure. Accidental exposure to peanuts is, however, frequent[14], even in people whose allergy has been proven in a DBPCFC.[30]

Reports have often mentioned that people have been reassured about the absence of peanut from a meal, only to find out, after the meal caused a reaction, that it did indeed contain peanut or was prepared on a board or using a knife previously used to prepare a peanut dish.[53] Some of these accidental exposures have been fatal.[35,36] In many cases, inadvertent exposure to peanut can be discovered by simple direct enquiry or detective work. In less stringently observed reactions, an obvious source of peanut protein is not determined. In many of these cases peanut oil has been blamed for the reaction, but there are conflicting views regarding the allergenicity of peanut oil (see below).

It has been shown on several occasions that the processing or heating of peanuts and peanut products does not decrease the allergenicity of the product significantly.[54-57] The safety or lack of safety of finished and processed peanut products has been addressed in two key studies, which have assessed the issue of accidental exposure to hidden peanut antigens.[55,56]

Nordlee tested 19 different peanut products and peanut oils by the method of RAST inhibition, which assumes that the presence of peanut in a test sample is established if it prevents the binding to peanut protein of serum IgE from peanut-allergic individuals. These products included peanut flour, peanut butter, peanut oil and peanut-butter-flavoured crisps. Peanut oil and hydrolysed peanut protein were shown not to contain peanut allergen, and peanut whole flour was shown to contain very small amounts. The other products significantly inhibited IgE binding, suggesting high levels of allergenicity.[55]

Keating[56] studied the application of immunological methods to the determination of industrial safety of catering equipment. This work involved sampling both food-processing materials and finished peanut-containing foods including M&M chocolates. Keating also studied virgin vegetable oil and vegetable oil that has been used to roast peanuts. It was possible to show that peanut protein was retrievable from oils and foods that had been deliberately "spiked" with peanut protein, but not, however, from the oil before its use to roast peanuts.

Peanuts have been used in the past in a deflavoured form, having been reflavoured and sold as other types of nuts such as walnuts and almonds. It is cheaper for industry to deflavour and reflavour peanuts than to use the original more expensive tree nuts[56] (though heightened public and commercial awareness of food allergy will probably decrease the opportunistic use of an allergenic food when a safer alternative exists). Food-processing errors may therefore expose peanut-allergic people to high doses of peanut through oversight or lack of awareness but also, through inadequate quality control, to low doses that can still cause reactions. The issues of food-processing safety and product labelling are dealt with in other chapters.

AMOUNT OF PEANUT NEEDED TO CAUSE REACTION

Experience suggests that the amount of protein needed to cause a reaction in mild or moderate reactors (severe reactors are not challenged) in a DBPCFC is between 50 and 100 mg of protein.[57,58,59] This is a fact that is beginning to achieve significant importance owing to the industrial application of immunological methods to determine safety and quality control mechanisms in the industry. Recent reports suggest that peanut protein can be detected at concentrations as low as 2 parts per million.[60]

It may be that one of the reasons that peanut-allergic subjects are so vulnerable to accidental exposure is that they react to very small doses of peanut, whereas people with other food allergies can consume larger doses of the relevant foods before a reaction occurs. We have data (unpublished) that show that peanut-allergic subjects react to doses of peanut protein below 50 mg and that there is an in vivo relationship between dose of peanut and severity of reaction. In another study of peanut oils, we challenged 56 subjects with peanut and only 1/35 subjects who had reported previous severe reactions suffered a comparable reaction under a controlled challenge setting (see Table 4.III).[37]

PEANUT OIL AND 'GOURMET' OILS

In the United Kingdom, 1.9 million tonnes of oil seed are crushed each year (data of the Seed Crushers' and Oil Processors' Associations, SCOPA). The majority of this is rapeseed (58%), followed in frequency by soya (28%) and sunflower (5%). Linseed constitutes approximately 3% of the total and all other oils constitute about 2% of production. The figures for the actual processing of the oils in the UK are slightly different; the total volume of vegetable oils processed in the UK is 1.3 million tonnes per annum. Again, rapeseed oil constitutes the largest group, with 34%, followed by palm oil at 27%, sunflower oil at 12% and soya-bean oil at 9%.

It can be seen that peanut does not figure in the top five types of seed crushed or types of oil processed. Most vegetable oils go into the manufacture of table spreads and speciality baking. Domestic and catering oil makes up about 12% and industrial frying uses up approximately 11% of oil consumed.

The processing of seed or nut oils starts with the cleaning and drying of the native nuts. The nuts are broken and flaked before being steam-heated and squeezed (expelled or pressed). This simple process results in the production of crude oil. This crude oil can be solvent-extracted before undergoing degumming, neutralising, washing and hydrogenation. These processes remove volatile fatty acids, esters and other impurities, which would compromise the quality and cause flavouring of refined oil.

Oils of other seeds and nuts are deliberately left relatively unrefined in order to enhance the flavour of foods (often salad dressings) to which they are added. These crude or so-called "gourmet" oils include walnut, brazil, hazel, almond and sesame-seed oil. It has been known for a long time that sesame-seed oil is a hazard to sesame-allergic individuals[61,62] The so-called gourmet oils have recently been shown to contain appreciable amounts of protein, in contrast to refined peanut oil.[63] Current scientifically based medical advice regarding the safety of peanut oils is based on three small studies of the protein content of peanut oils: two clinical[30,64] and one laboratory-based.[65]

Bock & Atkins gave up to 30 ml of refined peanut oil to four subjects who had previously reacted on DBPCFC with peanut. None reacted to refined peanut oil.[30]

Taylor[64] studied ten adult peanut-allergic subjects in a double-blind crossover study of peanut oil, with olive oil as the placebo. The subjects were well characterised, with positive histories, skin prick tests, and tests for peanut-specific serum IgE. The subjects appeared typical and representative, in that all had had exposures and reactions to peanut within the last 5 years. Seven had suffered mild reactions and three had reacted moderately. All of them had negative skin prick tests with the peanut oils. The subjects ingested peanut oil encapsulated in glycerin capsules, in doses of 1, 2 and 5 ml. No patient reacted to the oils, and the conclusion and title of the paper was "Peanut oil is not allergenic to peanut allergic individuals".[64]

The contrasting title of a paper by Hoffman & Collins-Williams[65] was: "Cold-pressed peanut oils may contain peanut allergen". This in vitro study isolated antigenic proteins from various types of peanut oil with corn oil and soya-bean oil as controls. The authors showed that there were easily detectable amounts of peanut protein (3.3 mg/ml) in cold pressed peanut oil.[65] To consume 50 mg of peanut protein (generally considered the minimum provoking dose in DBPCFCs) in crude peanut oil would, however, require a subject to drink more than 15 litres of crude peanut oil. The refined oils tested contained no peanut protein and did not bind IgE from a peanut-allergic serum. This in vitro study suggests that there may be variability in reactions to refined oils and cold-pressed, relatively impure oils.

This finding supports Keating,[56] who showed that refined oil contained no detectable peanut protein unless peanuts were cooked in the oil, after which peanut protein was detectable. In a similar real-life situation, the re-use of an unspecified vegetable oil to cook potato chips after cooking fish is considered to have caused the death of a fish-allergic subject[35] (case 7 in ref 35).

It is impossible to say what may be the frequency of re-use of peanut oils, but the purity and handling of the oils appear to be of equal importance. It may be that pure oils, when used properly, are safe, but if used to cook peanuts, become adulterated with peanut protein and therefore become potentially unsafe.[56] It is reasonable to speculate that the blaming of peanut oil for reactions may actually be putting the blame on the messenger (peanut oil) rather than the message (the peanut protein) - the oil itself being safe unless contaminated or adulterated with peanut protein from peanuts. Commercial sources state that crude oil is not available to the general public and is only used in foods in which peanut flavours are specifically required, such as satay sauces and, for example, in health-food bars (J Hancock, Anglia Oils, personal communication). Such foods should be clearly labelled as being peanut-flavoured and containing peanuts.

Pure oils do not appear to pose much of a risk to peanut-allergic individuals. A far greater risk is the inadvertent contamination of such an oil with peanuts. It is notable that in Taylor's study of refined oil no subject was skin prick test positive with the brand of peanut oil used.[67] Crude and cold-pressed oil do not appear to have been used for skin prick testing or in a food challenge.

We recently compared the in vivo allergenicity of two peanut oils - crude peanut oil and refined peanut oil - in a double-blind, crossover trial, involving 60 proven peanut-allergic subjects.[37] In contrast to Taylor's study,[64] where 7/10 had mild disease, 35/60 (58.3%) of the subjects we challenged reported severe previous reactions, usually in the form of a wheezy reaction to an exposure to peanut. In fact, only 5 (8.3%) of our subjects had suffered only mild reactions before. This was also the first occasion that peanut-allergic subjects had been challenged with crude peanut oil.

No subject showed a positive reaction to skin testing with the native crude or refined oil. Six subjects (10%) reacted to challenge with crude oil, although only two of these reactions were unequivocal - one subject wheezed and the other developed lip swelling. The other four reactions to crude oil were subjective, such as itching in the throat or lip tingling, without observable or measurable changes in physiological parameters. In marked contrast to the crude oil, no reaction occurred after challenge with the refined peanut oil in any of the 60 people tested, either subjectively or objectively. This demonstrates (with a 95% likelihood) that peanut oil represents a risk to less than 5% of peanut-allergics.[66] Though statistically robust and compelling, our study[37] does not prove that it is completely safe for caterers to use refined peanut oil. Every peanut-allergic person is at risk from the use of peanuts in cooking in restaurants and other people's homes, irrespective of whether the cooks use refined peanut oil or other vegetable oils. It is important that catering and restaurant staff are aware that the re-use of oils poses a risk to people with life-threatening reactions to foods, especially after they have been used to cook common allergenic foods. Subjects allergic to any peanuts, tree nuts, fish and shellfish, in particular, must be protected from any exposure to that food and to any oil used to cook that food for someone else.[35]

SUMMARY

Peanut is the most common cause of food-related anaphylaxis and food-related anaphylactic deaths. The diagnosis is easily made on the clinical history. Peanut allergy appears to manifest itself relatively early in life and is being recognised with increasing frequency. The roles of in utero or post-natal sensitisation are uncertain. It is not known what determines whether or not peanut allergy remits in later life. There is controversy surrounding the role of peanut oil in sensitisation and the causation of reactions.

The development of transgenic foods, including members of the legume family, means that the issue of cross-reactivity between peanuts and tree nuts must be addressed. Laboratory (RAST inhibition) studies of the effects of tree-nut proteins on peanut-allergic serum will be needed to address this question, and sensitive assays to detect low levels of peanut will help to improve food safety. Labelling requirements may need to change to acknowledge both the demonstration of safety of refined peanut oil for the majority of peanut-allergic individuals and the contrasting danger of crude peanut oil.

REFERENCES

1.   Changes in asthma prevalence: two surveys 15 years apart.
      Burr ML, Butland BK, King S, Vaughan-Williams E.
      Archives of Disease in Childhood 1989; 64: 1452-6.

2.   Evidence for an increase in atopic disease and possible causes.
      Bousquet J, Burney P.
      Clin. Exp. Allergy 1993; 23(6): 504-11.

3.   Increase in hospital admission for childhood asthma: trends in referral,
      severity and readmission from 1970 to 1985 in a health region of the United
      Kingdom.
      Anderson HR.
      Thorax 1989; 44: 614-9.

4.   Peanut allergy (letter).
      Ewan P
      BMJ 1996;313: 300.

5.   Peanut and nut allergy (letter).
      Wilson JA.
      BMJ 1996; 313: 299.

6.   Early history and origin of the peanut in Peanut: Culture and Uses: A
      Symposium. American Peanut Research and Education Foundation
      Association Inc.
      Hammons RO.
      Stillwater, Oklahoma, 1973.

7.   The many faces of the peanut
      Saavedro-Deogado AM
      Allergy Proceedings 1989: 10: 291-4.

8.   Peanut allergy in relation to heredity, maternal diet and other atopic
      diseases: results of a questionnaire survey, skin prick testing and food
      challenges.
      Hourihane JO'B, Dean TP, Warner JO
      BMJ 1996;313:518-21.

9.   Sensitization to peanut before 4 months - based upon 125 cases (English abstract).
     Hatahet R, Kirch F, Kanny G, Moneret-Vautrin DA
     Revue Française d'Allergologie et d'Immunologie Clinique 1994; 34 (5):377-81.

10. Prospective estimation of IgG, IgG subclass and igE antibodies to pdietary proteins in infants with cow milk allergy. Levels of antibodies to ehole milk protein, BLG and ovalbumin in relation to repeated milk challenge and clinical course of cow milk allergy
     Host A, Husby S, Gjesing B, Larsen JN, Lowenstein H
     Allergy 1992;47;218-29

11. Is deficiency of interferon-gamma production by allergen triggered cord blood cells a predictor of atopic eczema?
     Warner JA, Miles EA, Jones AC. Quint DJ, Colwell BM, Warner JO.
     Clin. Exp. Allergy 1994; 24: 423-30.

12. Prenatal allergen contact with milk proteins .
     Szepfalusi Z, Nentwitch I, Gerstmayr M, Jost E, Todoran L, Gratzl R, Herkner K, Urbanek R
     Clin. Exp. Allergy 1997;27 (1):28-35.

13. Secretion of peanut allergens in breast milk of nursing mothers (Abstract).
     De Bolt MFH, Johansen KL, Yunginger JW.
     J. Allergy Clin. Immunol. 1993; 93(1 part 2): 342.

14. Clinical characteristics of peanut allergy.
     Hourihane JO'B, Kilburn SA, Dean TP, Warner JO
     Clin. Exp. Allergy 1997;27:634-639.

15. Effect of combined maternal and infant food-allergen avoidance on development of atopy in early infancy:a randomized study.
     Zeiger RS, Heller S, Mellon MH, Forsythe AB, O'Connor RD, Hamburger RN, Schatz M
     J. Allergy Clin. Immunol. 1989;84: 72-89.

16. Clinical study of peanut and nut allergy in 62 consecutive patients: new features and associations.
     Ewan P.
     BMJ 1996; 312: 1074-8.

17.   Sensitisation to peanut and vitamin D oily preparations (Letter).
       De Montis G, Genobel D, Chemillier Truong M, Dupont C.
       Lancet 1993;341:1411.

18.   Risks of milk formulas containing peanut oils contaminated with peanut all
       infants with atopic dermatitis.
       Moneret-Vautrin, Hatahet R, Kanny G
       Pediatr Allergy Immunol 1994;5; 84-188.

19.   Etude expérimentale de la sensitation à l'arachide chez les cobayes (English
       abstract).
       Sabbah A, Lauret MG.
       Allergie et Immunologie 1994; 10: 380-2.

20.   Creams and ointments containing peanut oil may lead to sensitisation
       (letter).
       Lever LR
       BMJ 1996; 313:299

21.   Baby massage oils could be a hazard.
       Joyce R, Frosh A
       BMJ 1996;313:299.

22.   Peanut oil in medications (letter)
       Weeks R
       Lancet 1996; 348:759-60.

23.   Allergy to peanut (letter).
       Morris M, Smith S
       Lancet 1996; 348:1522.

24.   Allergy to peanut (letter).
       Barras N
       Lancet 1996; 348:1522.

25.   An overview of food hypersensitivity.
       James JM, Sampson HA.
       Pediatr. Allergy Immunol. 1992; 3: 667-78.

26.   Prevalence of food allergy and intolerance in the adult Dutch population.
       Niestijl Jansen JJ, Kardinaal AFM, Huijbers G, Vliegg-Boerstra BJ,
       Martens BPM, Ockhuizen T.
       J. Allergy Clin. Immunol. 1994; 93: 446-56.

27. A population study of food intolerance.
Young E, Stoneham MD, Petruckevitch A, Barton J, Rona R.
Lancet 1994; 343: 1127-30.1

28. Double-blind, placebo-controlled food challenge (DBPCFC) as an office procedure: a manual.
Bock SA, Sampson HA, Atkins FM, Zeiger RS, Lehrer S, Sachs M, Bush RK, Metcalfe DD
J. Allergy Clin. Immunol. 1988; 82(6):986-97

29. Cohort study of peanut and tree nut sensitisation by age of 4 years.
Tariq SM, Stevens M, Matthews S, Ridout S, Twiselton R, Hide DW.
BMJ 1996; 313: 514-17.

30. The natural history of peanut allergy.
Bock SA, Atkins FM.
J Allergy Clin Immunol 1989; 83: 900-4.

31. The natural history of peanut allergy (abstract).
Bock SA
J. Allergy Clin. Immunol. 1995; 95(1, pt2): 303.

32. Anaphylactic emergencies in Munich in 1992 (Abstract).
Bresser H, Sandner C, Rakoski J.
J. Allergy Clin. Immunol. 1995; 1(pt 2): 368.

33. The incidence, aetiology and management of anaphylaxis presenting to an Accident and Emergency department.
Stewart AG, Ewan PW.
QJ Med. 1996; 89: 859-64.

34. Incidence of severe food reactions in Colorado.
Bock SA, Dorion B.
J. Allergy Clin. Immunol. 1992; 90(4,pt1):683-5.

35. Fatal food-induced anaphylaxis.
Yunginger JW, Sweeney KG, Sturner WQ et al.
JAMA 1988; 260: 1450-2.

36. Fatal and near fatal anaphylactic reactions to food in children and adolescents.
Sampson HA, Mendelson L, Rosen JP.
New Eng. J. Med. 1992; 327: 380-4.

37.　Randomised, double-blind, crossover challenge study of allergenicity of peanut oils in subjects allergic to peanuts .
Hourihane JO'B, Bedwani SJ, Dean TP, Warner JO
BMJ 1997;314:1084-8.

38.　Risk of systemic reactions in patients taking beta blocking drugs receiving allergen immunotherapy injections
Hepner MJ, Ownby DR, Anderson JA et al
J Allergy Clin Immunol 1990; 86:407-11

39.　Association between the renin angiotensin system and anaphylaxis.
Hermann K, Ring J
In: Tissue renin-angiotensin systems
Eds. AK Mukhopadhyay, MK Raizada.
New York: Plenum Press, 1995, 299-309.

40.　Exercise induced anaphylaxis related to specific foods.
Tilles S, Schocket AL, Milgrom H.
J. Pediatrics 1995; 127: 587-9.

41.　Allergy to pollen and apple and cross-reactivity of the allergens studied with the RAST.
Lahti A, Bjorksten F, Hannuksela M.
Allergy 1980; 35: 297.

42.　Das "Sellerie-Karotten - Beifuss Gewurz-Syndrom" Hauttest-und RAST-Ergebnisse.
Schweiz. Med. Wochenschrift 1985; 115: 358-64.
Wuthrich B, Dietschi R.
Quoted in: Common allergenic structures in hazelnut, rye grain, sesame seeds, kiwi and poppy seeds.
Vocks E, Borga A, Szliska C, Serfert HU, Serfert B, Buron G, Borelli S.
Allergy 1993; 48: 168-72.

43.　Allergy to pistachio nuts.
Jansen A, de Rudt J de L, van Toorenenbergen AW, van Wijk RG.
Allergy Proceedings 1992; 12(5): 255-58.

44.　Pistachio nut hypersensitivity: identification of pistachio nut allergens.
Parra FM, Guevas M, Leguan A, Alonso MD, Beristain AM, Losada E.
Clin. Exp. Allergy 1993; 23: 996-1001.

45.   Allergenic cross-reactions among legume foods - an in-vitro study.
      Barnett D, Bonham B, Harden MEH.
      J. Allergy Clin. Immunol. 1987; 79: 433-38.

46.   Identification of a major peanut allergen, Ara h I, in patients with atopic
      dermatitis and positive peanut challenges.
      Burks AW, Williams LW, Helm RM, Connaughton C, Cockrell G, O'Brien
      T.
      J. Allergy Clin. Immunol. 1991; 88: 172-9.

47.   Recombinant peanut allergen Ara h I expression and IgE binding in patients
      with peanut hypersensitivity.
      Burks AW, Cockrell G, Stanley JS, Helm RM, Bannon GA.
      J. Clin. Invest. 1995; 96: 1715-21.

48.   Identification of unique antigenic fractions of soy and peanut (Abstract).
      Eigenmann PA, Burks AW, Bannon GA, Sampson HA.
      J. Allergy Clin. Immunol. 1996; 1(part 3): 328.

49.   Peanut antigen Ara h I: identifying the clinically relevant epitopes
      (Abstract).
      Bannon GA, Stanley JS, Cockrell G, Helm RM, Sampson HA, Burks AW.
      J. Allergy Clin. Immunol. 1996; 97(1 part 3): 330.

50.   Cloning and sequency of a walnut (Juglans regia) food allergen and its
      sequence similarity with other seed storage proteins.
      Teuber SS, Dandehor AM, Peterson WR, Watson SL.
      J. Allergy Clin. Immunol. 1996; 97(1, pt3): 241.

51.   Identification of a brazil nut allergen in transgenic soybeans.
      Nordlee JA, Taylor SL, Townsend JA, Thomas LA, Bush RK.
      New Eng. J. Med. 1996; 334(11): 688-92

52.   Clinical and immunological characteristics of Brazil nut allergy.
      Arshad SH, Malmberg E, Krapf K, Hide DW.
      Clin. Exp. Allergy 1991; 21: 373-6.

53.   Managing peanut allergy (editorial).
      Sampson HA
      BMJ 1996;312:1050-1.

54. Detection of allergy to nuts by the radioallergosorbent test.
Gillespie DN, Nakajima S, Glesch GJ.
J. Allergy Clin. Immunol. 1976; 57: 302-.

55. Allergenicity of various peanut products as determined by RAST inhibition
Nordlee JA, Taylor SL, Jones RT
J. Allergy Clin. Immunol. 1981;68:376-82.

56. Immunoassay of peanut allergens in food processing materials and finished foods.
Keating MU, Jones RT, Worley NJ, Shively CA, Yunginger JW.
J. Allergy Clin. Immunol. 1990; 86: 4-44.

57 Cottonseed hypersensitivity: New concerns over an old problem.
Atkins FM, Wilson M, Bock SA
J. Allergy Clin. Immunol. 1988; 82:242-50.

58. Peanut anaphylaxis (editorial).
Sampson HA.
J. Allergy Clin. Immunol. 1990: 86(1): 1-3.

59. Soy allergy in atopic children.
Magnolfi CF, Zani G, Lacava L, Patria MF, Bardare M
Ann. Allergy Asthma Immunol. 1996;77:197-201.

60. A sandwich enzyme-linked immunosorbent assay (ELISA) for the quantitation of peanut in foods (Abstract).
Taylor SL, Nordlee JA, Hefle SL.
J. Allergy Clin. Immunol. 1996; 97(1, pt3): 329.

61. Sensitivity to sesame seed and sesame oil.
Rubenstein L.
NY State JM 1950; 343-4.

62. Sesame seed oil anaphylaxis.
Chiu JT, Haydik IB.
J. Allergy Clin. Immunol. 1991; 88(3, pt 1): 414-5.

63. Allergenicity of gourmet nut oils processed by different methods (Abstract).
Teuber SS, Brown RL, Haapanen LAD.
J. Allergy Clin. Immunol. 1997; 99: 502-7.

64. Peanut oil is not allergenic to peanut-sensitive individuals.
Taylor SL, Busse WW, Sachs MI, Parker JL, Yunginger JW.
J. Allergy Clin. Immunol. 1981; 68: 372-5.

65. Cold pressed peanut oils may contain peanut allergen.
Hoffman DR, Collins-Williams C.
J. Allergy Clin. Immunol. 1994; 93: 801-2. 58.

66. Food and food additive intolerance in childhood.
David TJ.
Blackwell Scientific Publications, Oxford 1983.

5. LEGISLATION AND FOOD ALLERGIES

Jane Smith & Bernard O'Connor

INTRODUCTION

The potential for foods and food ingredients to cause allergic or hypersensitivity reactions in certain people, and how best to address the problem from a legislative point of view, are among the most debated topics in current food legislation.

Essentially, labelling is seen as the answer to the second issue, but exactly how should the appropriate labelling be given? It is believed that if foods are labelled in such a way as to inform the consumer that potentially allergenic or hypersensitive ingredients are present in a particular food, this may lessen the risk to affected consumers. Yet, at present, very few foods and food ingredients are thus labelled. Although labelling such as 'may contain X' or 'may contain traces of X', where 'X' is a potential allergen, can be seen on a range of food products, the use of such phrases is at the manufacturer's discretion and must take into account general provisions on misleading labelling.

Countries without detailed labelling legislation for allergens are now considering the need for its introduction; those where provisions are already in place are assessing their application and whether additional information is required. The problem is an international issue, so the labelling of potential allergens needs to be handled on an international basis. Focus is therefore on international bodies such as the European Commission and the Codex Alimentarius, as their proposals will be critical in future with respect to the introduction of any new labelling requirements. Restrictive barriers to trade in respect of such labelling will not assist the liberalising of free trade and would cause considerable problems for the manufacturer and exporter.

Part 1 of this chapter describes the major legislative requirements regarding food allergens and their labelling, where these are laid down, and assesses the possible future direction of such legislation. It also considers the gluten-free foods that are of importance to those with coeliac disease. Part 2 is concerned with the general obligations of manufacturers and their legal liabilities concerning the labelling of food allergies in nine European countries - namely, Austria, Belgium, Denmark, France, Germany, Greece, Portugal, Spain and the United Kingdom.

PART 1. LEGISLATIVE REQUIREMENTS

The EC Situation

Ensuring that the consumer is fully informed and protected from a public health point of view are key aspects of EC legislation. Barriers to trade are justifiable under the Treaty of Rome for public health and food safety issues;[1] the Member States are able to introduce such measures if deemed justified. At least one of the EU Member States has its own provisions on the labelling of allergens already in place and it is an issue in which the Commission is taking considerable interest. The European Parliament is keen to see labelling rules introduced in this area that would assist consumers further in making an informed choice concerning the foods they purchase.

General labelling requirements

General labelling at a European level is controlled by EC Directive 79/112/EEC, as amended by 86/197/EEC, 89/395/EEC, 91/72/EEC, 93/102/EC, 97/4/EC.[2] This Directive was developed using the principle of functional labelling, ensuring that consumers are presented with essential information as regards the nature of the product to ensure consumer safety and fair competition. Producers and manufacturers can give additional labelling information, provided this is accurate and does not mislead the consumer.

Ingredients listing

Under this Directive, ingredients of a prepacked product need to be labelled by their specific name in the ingredients list, unless exempted; in certain specified cases, generic names may be used instead; for example 'vegetable oil' may be given as a generic name in place of the specific type of oil used.

TABLE 5.I
Sample ingredients lists

Ingredients: Rehydrated textured vegetable protein (contains starch), Batter (contains wheatstarch, soya flour, raising agents: sodium bicarbonate, E450a; vegetable oil and hydrogenated vegetable oil, breadcrumbs, milk, onion, cheese, seasoning (contains flavourings), Stabilisers: E464, guar gum; wheatflour, garlic, salt, herbs, mustard powder, pepper.

Ingredients: Water, biscuit, cream, sugar, medium fat soft cheese, strawberries, vegetable oil and hydrogenated vegetable oil, egg, modified starch, wheat flour, yoghurt, dextrose, emulsifiers: E475, E471, E401, E322, colour: E163, gelling agent: pectin, acidity regulator E331, flavouring, antioxidant E327.

Table 5.I shows some sample ingredients lists. Another exemption to the labelling requirement is that the components of a compound ingredient need not be declared in the ingredients list of a prepacked food if that compound ingredient is present in a quantity of less than 25%, other than any additives present having a direct technological effect in the final food. Under this rule, therefore, many ingredients that have potential allergenic reactions but are present only in small quantities need not be specifically declared in the list of ingredients. Consumers who may be at risk are therefore not aware of their presence. The scope of the Directive is only for foods that are prepacked and are sold to the ultimate consumer or to catering establishments. Non-prepacked foods, including those sold at catering establishments, are currently outside the scope of the general labelling directive, so Member States may (or may not) have their own national labelling requirements for these. In any case, under current labelling laws, consumers are not required to be informed if non-prepacked foods contain potential allergens. A small number of food products still do not need to give an ingredients list, although the labelling of these products is currently under revision; the most significant product sector covered by this exemption is chocolate products.

The most recent amendment to 79/112/EEC, Directive 97/4/EC, includes a requirement that is of direct relevance to the allergy question.[3] Introduced by the European Parliament as an amendment to a text that was already in circulation, the requirement is now in place that, if the generic name 'modified starch' or 'starch' is used in the ingredients list, this must be accompanied by an indication of the specific vegetable origin of the starch or modified starch, where this may contain gluten. The amending directive will come into force 18 months after publication in the Official Journal of the European Communities, i.e. August 1998. National implementation will then follow, with Member States having until 14 February 2000 to prohibit products not complying. At the time of writing, none of the Member States has yet implemented this amending directive.

Allergen labelling

A further amendment to 79/112/EEC is already under discussion, which would concern the labelling of potential allergens when present as ingredients. In the opinion of the European Commission, consumers do not receive detailed information about the exact composition of the foodstuff they are buying, owing to the compound ingredients provisions, although they can still make an informed choice. However, the lack of such detailed information can be problematical to those with allergies or intolerance to certain substances, who need as much information about the product as possible. Although it is recognised that labelling for consumers in general must not be considered as the only source of information available, as the medical establishment is key in this respect, it is advisable to assist those with allergies or intolerance as much as possible by making more comprehensive information about the composition of products available to them. Therefore, it is considered necessary that certain substances recognised scientifically as being the source of allergies or intolerance be included in a list of ingredients and not qualify as exceptions under the compound ingredients provisions in the general labelling directive. The

Commission recognises that Member States can take their own action concerning foods sold in bulk or foods served in catering establishments. The draft proposal, Document III/5909/97,[4] dated January 1997, therefore proposes that exemptions from declaration in the list of ingredients do not apply to certain named ingredients recognised as causing allergic or intolerance reactions. The list of foods and ingredients recognised as causing hypersensitivity reactions in certain individuals and which must be declared in the list of ingredients is detailed in Table 5.II.

TABLE 5.II
Proposed list of allergenic foods

cereals containing gluten;
crustaceans;
eggs;
fish;
peanuts;
soya;
nuts;
sesame seeds;
sulfite in concentrations of 10 mg/kg or more

This document is at a very early stage of discussion, and it will inevitably be modified as Member States, industry, consumer groups and other interested parties are asked to comment on its content. The contribution of the European Parliament towards a final text will also be significant in agreeing such legislation. The list of foods bears a degree of similarity to that contained in a proposed revision to the Codex Alimentarius standard on labelling; it is likely that development of the two will continue to be parallel, since this issue is of interest internationally.

The Green Paper

A draft Green Paper on General Principles of Food Law in the European Union has been published for consultation with all the major parties in the food area, including industry, consumer groups, research bodies, trade associations and others, in an effort to come to some conclusions as to how European food law should develop in the future.[5] A final version is expected shortly. Criticisms have been made that current EC law is fragmented and does not really meet the needs and expectations of consumers, producers, manufacturers or traders. In order to continue to fulfil the basic requirements of providing a high level of protection of public health and safety, food labelling is reviewed as part of the Green Paper. The example of the Commission being asked to consider amending the labelling rules to provide for more information about the possible presence of known allergens in foods, even when present in very small or trace amounts, is used to illustrate how certain aspects of the current labelling rules may not provide sufficient information for the consumer in all cases, whereas other requirements have possibly become too detailed. The Commission is therefore requesting comment on whether current core mandatory labelling requirements are detailed enough and whether the right balance is struck between these and voluntary information given on food labels.

Food control programmes

The 1997 food control programme, as detailed in Commission Recommendation 97/77/EC of 8 January 1997,[6] under article 14 (3) of Directive 89/397/EEC,[7] the Official Control Directive, recommends that, during 1997, Member States take samples and undertake laboratory analysis for the occurrence of potential allergens and products that cause hypersensitivity reactions as contaminants, primarily in products claimed as 'free from' a particular ingredient. Sampling is to be restricted to products described as not containing milk/milk proteins, lactose, egg or gluten. This study will survey the enforcement actions taken by the Member States when contaminated products are found on the market. Sample record sheets are included as part of the Decision in order to enhance comparability of results. This study is considered particularly important since foods labelled with claims implying the absence of certain protein ingredients are a serious potential health risk if they are contaminated with even small amounts of that material, and the study will indicate the scale of the problem. Under Directive 79/112/EEC,[2] labelling must not mislead the purchaser to a material degree. Data from this study will provide information to determine whether any further control activities in this area are needed in the future.

Allergens and novel ingredients

Commission Regulation (EC) No. 258/97 of 27 January 1997 on novel foods and novel food ingredients,[8] which is binding on the Member States of the EU and entered into force on 16 May, is intended to meet current concerns over the potential environmental impact of novel foods produced using modern techniques and the provision of consumer information for such products. Additional specific labelling requirements must be given when novel foods and ingredients covered by the Regulation are no longer equivalent to existing foods or ingredients in terms of their characteristics or food properties such as composition, nutritional value or nutritional effects or intended use. The final consumer must also be informed of the presence in the novel food or food ingredient of material that is not present in an existing equivalent foodstuff and which may have implications for the health of certain sectors of the population. It is possible that proteins used in novel food ingredients or in ingredients derived from genetically modified organisms (GMOs) may be potential allergens or have the potential to cause hypersensitivity, which would not be present in the original, unmodified ingredient. This aspect of technological development is therefore significant when considering further potential allergen problems.

EU Member State National Laws

In the absence of harmonised provisions on allergen labelling at EC level, the national provisions of the individual Member States need to be addressed. A summary of major national Member State provisions specifically on allergen labelling is presented in Table 5.III. While the UK and Germany have no specific provisions, the information detailed below may be of interest to manufacturers, together with the more detailed information provided by Sweden and Finland.

TABLE 5.III
Summary of major national Member State provisions
specifically on allergen labelling

Country	Allergen labelling
EC	draft in preparation
UK	none
Germany	none
Sweden	guidelines
Finland	regulations
France	none
Netherlands	none
Spain	none

United Kingdom

There are currently no specific provisions under UK legislation concerning the labelling of potential food allergens. The Food Safety Act 1990 requires that food must be of the nature, substance or quality demanded by the purchaser and comply with food safety requirements.[10] In addition, labelling must not be misleading to the consumer.

The Food Labelling Regulations 1996, SI 1996 No. 1499, control the mandatory labelling requirements for foods.[11] These implement the general provisions of 79/112/EEC, but there are no specific references to the labelling of allergen ingredients. However, the Ministry of Agriculture, Fisheries and Food (MAFF) drew attention to the labelling of food containing nuts in draft guidance notes to the 1996 Regulations; the draft notes recommended that, if the presence of nuts was not clear from the product name, the ingredients list or the way in which the food was presented, an appropriate warning should be given on the label - for example a 'contains nuts' declaration placed prominently on the label or a 'new recipe' declaration, which would warn the consumer to look at the ingredients list more closely. These comments never reached the final published version of the guidance notes, possibly owing to developments at EC level. In the UK, at this time, some manufacturers choose to give a declaration 'contains nuts' or 'may contain traces of peanuts'. Provided the general requirements of the Food Safety Act and the Food Labelling Regulations are not contravened, such labelling can be acceptable.

Under the General Product Safety Regulations 1994, requirements are imposed concerning the safety of products, including food, intended for consumers;[12] a producer is required to provide information to consumers and adopt measures to inform them of risks that a product might present. The application of this regulation in terms of allergen labelling is not clear, in view of existing controls by means of the Food Safety Act; however, manufacturers should be aware of the requirements therein. Products complying with existing comprehensive UK national safety legislation are safe products for the purpose of these regulations, unless the contrary is proved.

Hazard warning procedures are in operation for food allergies in the UK, particularly when the allergenic compounds are present as a result of contamination. Under the UK Food Hazard Warning System, set out in Food Safety Act Code of Practice No. 16,[13] which applies to food actually or allegedly not meeting food safety requirements, hazard warnings are issued by the Department of Health and its territorial equivalents relating to allergies as a matter of policy. This is due to the argument that, for susceptible individuals, foods containing undeclared ingredients to which they are allergic do not meet food safety requirements and therefore hazards arising involving those foods should be subject to the hazard warning system. Therefore, enforcement authorities have been asked to ensure that any food allergy problems discovered by enforcement officers or notified to them by food businesses are passed on to the Department of Health or its territorial equivalent, so that a hazard warning can be issued. This applies in respect of contamination or problems that may have occurred during food labelling. The key issue for industry to consider here is the importance of communication with the appropriate authorities so that the necessary steps can be taken by all parties to lessen any potential impact. Notification procedures are currently under review, as part of an overall revision of the Food Safety Act Codes of Practice.

The draft Industry Guide to Good Hygiene Practice for the Retail Industry provides guidance on compliance with the Food Safety (General Food Hygiene) Regulations 1995 and the Food Safety (Temperature Control) Regulations 1995 for the retail sector, as well as including advice on good practice and additional background information on general food hygiene matters. The issue of contamination, where potential allergens are inadvertently included in food products, is referred to when considering physical and chemical contamination, owing to the special care needed to be taken in such instances.

Germany

There are no guidelines or regulations on the labelling of foodstuffs that may cause allergic reactions, or of substances that may cause a hypersensitive reaction. The Federal Ministry of Health has indicated that it welcomes the efforts now underway to deal with this issue, but does not plan at present to draw up any specific provisions. In common with other countries, statements such as 'does not contain nuts' could be a problem under product liability laws, if small amounts of nut were inadvertently included and caused an allergic reaction.

Sweden

In contrast, Sweden is an EU Member State with detailed guidelines on allergen labelling. Under the Swedish labelling regulations, the compound ingredient rule in the EC General Labelling Directive 79/112/EEC is applicable.[14] However, if the compound ingredient is listed only with its name, it is desirable that ingredients that may cause hypersensitivity reactions are always stated in the list of ingredients. Examples of such ingredients given in the 1997 Guidelines on the Labelling of Foods are gluten-containing grain, eggs, milk, fish, nuts, leguminous plants (e.g. soya beans, peanuts and peas), and sulfite.[15] For example, the labelling could be given in the form 'margarine (contains milk)' or 'mayonnaise (with eggs)'. Although some consumers may be aware that these foods are likely to contain such components, others may be less so. It is also recommended that the same guidance is applied to additives that may cause hypersensitivity reactions, which should always be declared in the list of ingredients, for example antioxidants, colours, preservatives. Although additives are declared in compound foods if they have a technological effect in the final foods, if they are present only by carry-over and are not technologically effective, their declaration is not required under current laws.

An amendment to the Swedish labelling laws, dated 1995, included changes to the guidelines on the use of certain claims.[16] It is now stipulated that labelling may not contain expressions, symbols or other information suggesting that ordinary foods are intended for particular nutritional purposes. 'Naturally gluten-free', 'free from milk', 'without soya' and 'suitable for allergenics' are given as specific examples of expressions that should not be used on ordinary foods. Symbols with such meaning should also not be used.

Finland

The Finnish labelling regulations include certain requirements for the declaration of potentially allergenic ingredients, as part of the provisions regarding the declaration of compound ingredients.[17] A compound ingredient may be declared by its own name, provided that the list of its own ingredients and additives immediately follows this name. If the compound ingredient represents less than 25% of the ingredients used in the final product, at least the 'active' additives and those ingredients that can produce symptoms of hypersensitivity in an individual using the foodstuff must be declared. The following at least must be declared in this respect: peas, fish, eggs, milk, soya beans and crustaceans, and products manufactured from them; peanuts, almonds and nuts; and oats, barley, rye and wheat.

The International Scene

There are a number of countries on an international basis whose regulations contain provisions on the labelling of foods containing potential allergens, or whose regulatory authorities have made reference to labelling of allergens.

USA

Of particular interest is the Food and Drug Administration (FDA) position in this respect. In June 1996, the Center for Food Safety and Applied Nutrition issued a Notice to Manufacturers concerning the Label Declaration of Allergenic Substances in Foods.[18]

The Food, Drug and Cosmetic Act requires, in virtually all cases, a complete ingredients listing on foods. Exceptions to this are that spices, flavourings and colourings may be declared collectively under the Act, without each individual one having to be specifically named; also, incidental additives, such as processing aids, that are present in foods at an insignificant level and do not have a technical or functional effect in the final food need not be declared, under Title 21 of the Code of Federal Regulations. The FDA, in this Notice, stressed to manufacturers that the exemption applied only when the incidental additive was present at an insignificant level and it must not have any technological effect in the final product. An example is quoted of egg white as a binder in breading on a breaded fish product; the egg white is not incidental as it is acting in the final food, so should be declared. As allergen problems can arise with very low levels of ingredients, the FDA is considering whether it is necessary to clarify the regulations to ensure that manufacturers fully understand the circumstances in which allergenic food ingredients must be declared and to ensure that sensitive individuals are protected by appropriate labelling. The FDA is also open to comment on how the problem of potential allergens in additives should be handled. It may consider it necessary to introduce rule-making for the labelling of allergenic ingredients.

While assessing the situation, the FDA, in the Notice, requests manufacturers to examine their product formulations for ingredients and processing aids containing known allergens that are currently exempted from declaration as incidental additives and to declare these in the ingredients statement. Where appropriate, the name of the ingredient may be accompanied by a parenthetical statement for clarity, for example '(processing aid)'. It is felt that allergenic ingredients in an additive could be declared in the correct position in the list (usually at the end, owing to their low levels), and other non-allergenic ingredients would continue to be exempt.

Examples of foods that are among those most commonly known to cause serious allergenic responses are, according to the FDA, milk, eggs, fish, crustacea, molluscs, tree nuts, wheat and legumes (in particular, soya beans and peanuts). The FDA advises that the issue of declaring allergenic ingredients in food is being discussed on an international level - a move that it welcomes.

Another area of concern to the FDA is cross-contamination so as to cause inadvertent addition or introduction of an allergenic ingredient into a product where it would not normally be found. For example, a product without peanuts could end up containing peanut traces. The FDA feels that labelling such as 'may contain peanuts' should not be used as a substitute for Good Manufacturing Practice (GMP); manufacturers are urged to take all steps to eliminate such contamination and ensure the absence of the allergenic food or ingredient. The FDA is considering options for providing consumers with further information in this respect and how this issue should be addressed.

The FDA has, however, in Part 105.62 of Title 21 of the Code of Federal Regulations,[19] established label statements required for foods represented as for specific dietary use owing to their having decreased, or absent, allergenic properties, or being offered as a substitute for a food with allergenic properties. Such labelling requirements include the common or usual name and proportion of each ingredient; a qualification of the name of the food, or of each ingredient, to reveal clearly the specific plant or animal source of each ingredient or food, if the specific source is not otherwise clear; and an informative statement of the nature and effect of any treatment or processing of the food or ingredient thereof, if the changed allergenic property results from such treatment or processing.

Australia

Under the Australian Food Standards Code,[20] Standard A1, compound ingredient provisions are detailed whereby, in common with the EC, if an ingredient contributes less than 250 g/kg (25%) of a food, food additives are the only components that must be declared. In contrast to EC law, unless specifically required, if an ingredient contributes less than 100 g/kg (10%) of a food, no components of the food need be declared. However, the Standard does require that the presence of peanuts must always be declared in a food. In addition, the standard on honey and related products (Standard K2) contains a definition for pollen and the requirement that packages containing a pollen product must declare on the label, in standard type of 3 mm, 'THIS PRODUCT MAY CAUSE SEVERE ALLERGIC REACTIONS'. Standard K2 also defines royal jelly and requires that royal jelly, or foods containing royal jelly, must include, immediately following the product name, in type of 3 mm, one of the statements below:-

For royal jelly -
'WARNING - THIS PRODUCT IS NOT RECOMMENDED FOR ASTHMA AND ALLERGY SUFFERERS AS IT CAN CAUSE SEVERE ALLERGIC REACTIONS'
For foods containing royal jelly -
'WARNING - THIS PRODUCT CONTAINS ROYAL JELLY AND IS NOT RECOMMENDED FOR ASTHMA AND ALLERGY SUFFERERS AS IT CAN CAUSE SEVERE ALLERGIC REACTIONS'.

Canada

The Canadian labelling regulations in the Food and Drugs Regulations include provisions concerning the use of generic or common names in the list of ingredients.[21] However, if peanut oil, hydrogenated or partially hydrogenated peanut oil or modified peanut oil are contained within the ingredient, they must be specifically listed in the ingredients list.

The Codex Alimentarius Position

At present, a Codex draft document that would amend the Codex General Standard for the labelling of prepackaged foodstuffs (Recommendations for the labelling of foods and ingredients that can cause hypersensitivity) is being discussed.[9] At the international Codex Committee on Food Labelling (CCFL) meeting in Canada in April 1997, this draft was advanced to Step 5, with an understanding that guidance was required on how to proceed with updating the list of substances capable of causing hypersensitivity requiring mandatory labelling.

The draft would amend the provision in the Codex General Standard regarding the declaration of compound ingredients in the ingredients list as follows:-

i)   by reducing the level at which the components of a compound ingredient do not have to be declared from when the compound ingredient is less than 25% to 5%, other than food additives that serve a technological function in the finished product and ingredients known to cause allergic or intolerance reactions;

ii) by including in the draft the following foods and ingredients that are known to cause hypersensitivity and that must always be declared as such:

cereals containing gluten, i.e. wheat, rye, barley, oats, spelt or their hybridised strains and products of these;

crustacea and products of these;

eggs and egg products;

fish and fish products;

peanuts, soya beans and products of these;

milk and milk products (lactose included);

tree nuts and nut products; and

sulfite in concentrations of 10 mg/kg or more

There may be changes in respect of the content of the draft before it is finally adopted, particularly in respect of the list of ingredients known to cause hypersensitivity. Certain countries are keen for celery and sesame seeds to be added to the list, including the UK for sesame seeds and Denmark for celery. Australia wishes to see royal jelly added. Some countries do not feel that it is necessary to reduce the level for exemption from compound ingredient declaration if there is to be a list of specific allergens drawn up that will always have to be declared, whatever their level. There is a problem with the proposed reduction of the compound ingredient level with the EU Member States, where, if this draft was to be carried forward, it would be in conflict with the provisions of the EC General Labelling Directive.[2] In contrast, more than one country has indicated that a level of less than 5% should be introduced. All countries seem to be in agreement that an expert body should be available to evaluate scientific evidence concerning allergenicity and to determine whether additions should be made to the proposed list. This aspect is likely to be given priority over the next year.

Gluten-free Foods

One of the allergens most widely found in foods is gluten. Since there are as yet no fully reliable tests which detect small quantities of gluten, the approach of regulatory authorities and of coeliac societies is empirical. Manufacturers and retailers do, sometimes, have their own schemes for the labelling of foods that are gluten-free, for example with a symbol indicating this. There may be no specific provisions in the legislation on such labelling, but general criteria concerning misleading labelling would have to be met, and it is necessary that strict manufacturing controls operate on such products. There may be coeliac societies in individual countries that have their own guidance on what should constitute a gluten-free food; their recommendations will be in addition to any regulatory provisions. However, there are provisions on gluten-free foods on a regulatory basis that are of interest.

The EC Position

Under EC Directive 89/398/EEC,[22] as amended, foods for particular nutritional uses, or PARNUTs foods, are defined as foods that, owing to their special composition or manufacturing process, are clearly distinguishable from foodstuffs for normal consumption, which are suitable for their claimed nutritional purpose and which are marketed in such a way as to indicate suitability. Currently, there are nine categories of PARNUTs foods listed in the annex to this Directive, one of which is gluten-free foods. The intention originally was to establish detailed compositional and labelling requirements on each of these categories of foods; however, only certain categories have so far been regulated in this way and there is ongoing discussion as to whether gluten-free foods and the other remaining categories should be included under the scope of this Directive at all. The latest information is that, following discussion by the Standing Committee on Foodstuffs, a short directive containing just a basic definition of a gluten-free food has been put forward as a Common Position text; this approach is understood to be backed by the majority of the Member States. This will have implications for the labelling of such products in that they will still be classified as PARNUTs foods and so be within the scope of labelling provisions detailed in the PARNUTs framework directive.

Until this amending directive is finalised, Member States may have their own provisions concerning the labelling of gluten-free foods.

Current Codex provisions

The Codex standard for gluten-free foods was amended in 1983 and proposals are well advanced for further amendment.[23] The scope of the standard is for those processed foods that have been specially prepared to meet the dietary needs of persons intolerant to gluten. The standard does not apply to foods that, in their normal form, do not contain gluten.

A gluten-free food is described as consisting of or containing as ingredients such cereals as wheat, triticale, barley, rye, oats, or their constituents, which have been rendered 'gluten-free', or in which any ingredients normally present containing gluten have been substituted by other ingredients not containing gluten. The descriptor 'gluten-free' means that the total nitrogen content of the gluten containing cereal grains used in the product is maximum 0.05 g/100 g of grains, on a dry matter basis. A further proviso is made that gluten-free foods substituting for important basic foods, such as flour or bread, must supply approximately the same amount of vitamins and minerals as the original foods they replace in accordance with the national legislation of the country in which the food is sold.

The proposed amendment states that the amount of gluten must not exceed 200 ppm in a 'gluten-free' food or ingredient, determined and calculated on a dry matter basis. It is also proposed that gluten-free foods that are substituting for basic foods supply approximately the same amount of vitamins and minerals as the foods they replace, without the need to be in accordance with the national legislation of the country of sale. In addition, the product is to be prepared with special care under Good Manufacturing Practice (GMP) to avoid contamination with prolamins.

The Codex standard requires the following in regard to labelling:-

✦ the term 'gluten-free' must be in immediate proximity to the name of the food;

✦ complete list of ingredients must be given, including the nature and source of starch present. For starch prepared from gluten-containing cereal grains, this declaration must be accompanied by 'containing not more than 0.3% protein in the dry matter';

✦ nutrition information must be given in the format specified;

✦ date marking and storage instructions must be included.

A food that naturally has no gluten may not be called 'gluten-free'; however, a cereal or food product containing a cereal that naturally has no gluten may be labelled to show that it is naturally free of gluten and is suitable for use in a gluten-free diet.

The international situation for gluten-free foods

On the international scene, a number of countries control the use of descriptions such as 'gluten-free' in food labelling and define such products.

France

Gluten-free foods in France are considered as dietetic products and fall under the scope of the Order of 20 July 1977 concerning dietetic and dietary products. Gluten-free foods are categorised as "foods completely or partially devoid of certain protein constituents and are foods manufactured from raw materials that have undergone special preparation to remove, in part or totally, some of the protein constituents, or using materials naturally free from these protein constituents, are used to replace the ingredients containing the proteins and which are normally present in the corresponding equivalent food".[24] The product description must indicate the main characteristic of the product; the phrase 'free from...' (exempt de...) must be given, where the name of the protein constituent is included. The name 'gluten' may be written in brackets if the protein in question is gliadin. For each protein constituent, the quantity in mg/100 g ready-to-consume product must be given on the label.

Switzerland

Gluten-free foods in Switzerland may only contain a maximum of 10 mg gliadin/100 g of the dry matter in accordance with the Swiss Food Code.[27] Foods thus described have the main gluten component replaced by another that does not naturally contain gluten, such as rice, soya, potato, or millet, or where the gluten has been extracted.

Israel

One country that does have detailed provisions on gluten-free foods is Israel. The Israeli regulation[25] defines gluten as plant protein found in the grains of wheat, rye, barley, oats and their by-products, including starches, malt and bran, and states that no food shall be manufactured containing gluten or to which gluten has been added in any proportion unless the ingredients list contains the name of the plant from which the gluten originates and the words 'contains gluten'. These provisions apply to imported foods as well as foods marketed in Israel.

The Israeli regulations on gluten labelling contain specific restrictions on the use of the term 'gluten-free' in food labelling. The descriptor 'gluten-free' may only be used if all the conditions below are met:-

i)   the food contains no gluten in any proportion whatsoever;

ii) the food is produced on a production line that is not used for the manufacture of food containing gluten;

iii) the appropriate steps have been taken to ensure that the product has not been contaminated with gluten.

It is unusual for provisions to be this specific; the main issue raised by this standard is whether it is necessary for a food claiming to be allergen-free to be manufactured on a dedicated production line, or whether Good Manufacturing Practice and Hazard Analysis Critical Control Point (HACCP) procedures should be sufficient when being carried out correctly.

Australia

The Australian Food Standards Code[20] includes a prescribed method of analysis for gluten determination (making reference to the second supplement of the Association of Official Analytical Chemists (AOAC) 15th edition, 1990). In addition, detailed claims provisions are laid down.

Standard A1 of the Australian Food Standards Code lays down the following claims provisions with respect to gluten:-

Gluten-free - such a claim must not be made unless the food contains starch, modified starch, thickener, cereal or a cereal derivative; does not contain any detectable gluten by the prescribed method of analysis; does not contain oats or any constituent of oats.

Low in gluten - such a claim must not be made *unless* the food contains starch, modified starch, thickener, cereal or a cereal derivative; contains maximum 0.2 g/kg gluten when analysed by the prescribed method; and does not contain oats or any constituent of oats.

Reduced gluten content - such a claim must not be made unless the food meets the criteria for a 'gluten-free' or 'low in gluten' claim and the claim is made in conjunction with the words 'gluten-free', 'low in gluten' or 'low-gluten', as appropriate.

A claim to the effect that a food does not contain added gluten must not be made.

Canada

Consumer and Corporate Affairs, Canada, in its nutrition claims and statements provisions within its Guide for Food Manufacturers and Advertisers,[26] defines 'gluten-free' as a term that may be applied when a food does not contain any wheat, oats, barley, rye or triticale. A specified symbol is given that can be used, but prior approval should be obtained from the Celiac Association in Canada.

Under the Canadian Food and Drug Regulations, when a 'gluten-free' claim is used, details of the energy value of the food, in calories and kJ, and the protein, fat and carbohydrate content of the food, in grams, must be given on the label, per serving of stated size of the food. The need to give nutrition information in order to inform the consumer about the nature of the product is important, as the nutritional profile of a gluten-free food may be quite different from that of one containing gluten.

Infant Feed

Owing to the potential sensitivity of very young children, particularly in respect of proteins, provisions on potential allergens are becoming a feature of recent legislation for infant milks and weaning foods. EC Directive 96/5/EC[28] on processed foods for babies and young children requires that information as to the presence or absence of gluten must be given if the indicated age from which the product may be used is below 6 months. Directive 91/321/EEC,[29] as amended, on infant formulae and follow-on formulae, allows for a claim to be made concerning the risk of allergy to milk proteins. This claim may include terms referring to reduced allergen or reduced antigen properties. In order for the claim to be made, the amount of immunoreactive protein measured with methods generally accepted as appropriate is less than 1% of nitrogen-containing substances in the formula. In addition, other compositional and labelling criteria must be met.

Conclusion

To conclude, therefore - legislation directly relating to potential allergens at present concerns how individual components should be declared in ingredients lists, and specific rules for indicating that a food is free of a particular allergen, e.g. gluten. Although provisions on allergen-free foods may continue to be developed, particularly in respect of infant feed, the key issue is how and to what extent ingredients with potential for hypersensitive or allergenic reactions should be declared on food products. One simple answer would be to remove the exemption relating to compound ingredients present at less than 25%, and require all ingredients at whatever level to be declared. This would, however, be difficult for manufacturers to deal with, particularly for products with limited room on the label. Some reduction in the 25% level, possibly to 5 or 10%, has been suggested in the past and may well prove a likely step forward in the future, as illustrated by the latest Codex proposals. A combination of this and specific declarations for potential allergens could improve the picture for consumers; however, if the ingredients list was lengthened, this might prove a barrier to consumer understanding and would make reading ingredients lists more difficult. One suggestion has been that allergens should be listed in a suitably conspicuous place, without the need for a more lengthy ingredients list. Restricting the use of generic names for ingredients could also help, by trying to ensure that the presence of potential allergens was not lost by the use of generic names. This would cause its own problems for manufacturers, however, particularly in respect of the supply of raw materials. This still leaves unsolved the question of the allergen content of non-packed foods and foods sold at catering establishments, for example meals at restaurants, which are currently outside the scope of general labelling regulations in many countries. Advances in scientific research may lead to additional ingredients or components of ingredients being identified as having a potential allergenic effect, and some form of procedure to enable such compounds to be added to any list quickly and effectively is seen as crucial.

Another issue of interest to regulators is whether allergen-free foods should be produced on dedicated production lines, as is currently practised in Israel, or whether Good Manufacturing Practice and HACCP procedures should be sufficient to ensure that contamination does not take place. This will continue to be a significant issue towards the next millennium.

Both Codex and EU provisions will continue to play an important role in future legislation in the area of food allergens; a number of countries, including Germany, have indicated their interest in developments at an international level, particularly with regard to the development of the Codex guidelines. It is likely that no significant increase in new legislation in this area will take place until a final document has been agreed.

Although specific labelling of allergens will improve information to consumers, there will continue to be the risk of undeclared allergenic substances in a food, and consumers will need to remain aware of this possibility. The potential range of adverse reactions from ingredients is very large, and it will have to be recognised that only those compounds giving severe reactions will be able to be specifically labelled.

PART 2. LEGAL LIABILITIES

Summary of Liability Issues

There is, in general, no obligation on manufacturers in the nine EC Member States examined to inform consumers of the presence of potential allergens in their products. However, if the manufacturer decides to inform the consumer, he will be liable if the information provided is inaccurate or incorrect unless it can be shown that the error was unavoidable.

Under common law, a manufacturer who is aware of the presence of an allergen in a given product, and for reasons of omission or deceit fails to warn the consumer may be liable to a consumer who suffers harm as a result of the use of that product.

Manufacturers are generally liable for the quality and safety of their products under general civil and common law provisions as well as specific consumer protection legislation, product safety regulations and product liability laws, which all place a high duty of care on manufacturers.

General Obligations of the Manufacturer

Austria

Austrian law does not explicitly require manufacturers to inform consumers who suffer from intolerances to certain foods. Legal provisions regarding information obligations in respect of allergies exist only for nickel products.

However, this absence of explicit legal provisions does not exempt manufacturers from certain obligations concerning "information on tolerance to certain food". Among these obligations are the following rules:

✦ The marketing of noxious food is prohibited. A noxious product is one that causes trouble to an average healthy person. As allergies are rare and are defined according to medical standards, the marketing and distribution of food that could cause allergic reactions are not prohibited.

✦ Austrian law on product liability provides that manufacturers are obliged to draw the user's attention to dangerous attributes or possible dangerous uses of the product. The producer must provide information if it is expected that the product will be consumed by those unfamiliar with the risks involved, but warnings of risks that are within the range of general experience are not required. Consequently, manufacturers are obliged to inform consumers of allergy risks only if and in so far as the food intolerance is untypical and generally unknown to the person concerned.

✦ The amount of information that a manufacturer must give to a contracting party exceeds the amount of information given to unknown consumers. If the contracting party is the consumer of the product and the manufacturer knows about the party's allergy, the manufacturer must warn the party of potential consequences even in cases of a typical allergy.

When the manufacturer voluntarily chooses to provide information about possible intolerances, this information must be true and correct. Misleading indications or statements may cause liability problems.

Under Austrian law, all "health-related" indications are prohibited. Examples of prohibited statements are references to medical histories, medical recommendations, expert opinions, etc. Exemptions from this prohibition include reference to the compatibility of food for dietary use for allergic people. However, this may only be used after the Ministry of Health has been adequately informed.

In the case of voluntary information, the manufacturer will be liable if the information is not accurate. However, false advice negligently given to third persons does not incur responsibility. Nevertheless, there are certain exemptions to this principle, and a person who provides the information realising that the given information would be used to satisfy legitimate interests of a third person will be considered liable for the accuracy of the information. As the manufacturer knows that the information he sends will be used by people suffering from allergies, he can also be held liable for negligence.

Belgium

Under Belgian law, there is no specific regulation obliging food manufacturers to inform consumers about the allergen content of a food product. There is a statutory obligation to label the ingredients, but no obligation to warn consumers that one of those ingredients could trigger an allergy.

However, Belgian law regarding "fair commercial practices" imposes on the seller of a product the obligation to disclose to the buyer correct and useful information about the characteristics of the product or service, considering the intended use or the reasonably foreseeable use by the buyer. The seller will be in breach of his legal duty to inform if he does not disclose that information. These provisions, although applicable to the parties of a commercial transaction, could not be used by an information-gathering organisation to force manufacturers to provide them with information on the exact content of the food.

Other legislation that could be of relevance to the problem of allergens in foodstuffs is that on consumer protection.

Belgian legislation on consumer safety, in addition to the laws on unfair commercial practices, imposes on the manufacturer the obligation to provide accurate information enabling the consumer to evaluate the risks that may arise from the use of the product in regular conditions or in situations reasonably foreseen by the manufacturer. These regulations also impose on the manufacturer the obligation to market safe products. In order to comply with this general obligation of safety, the manufacturer is under a duty of due diligence. Once the product has been marketed, the manufacturer has to be involved in the follow-up of the product's safety.

A product is considered defective under Belgian law when it does not provide consumers with the safety they can legitimately expect, considering all circumstances and especially the presentation of the product and the regular use or reasonably foreseen use of the product. However, the fact that a product contains ingredients capable of triggering allergies may not be enough to consider that product defective.

Belgian courts have developed in their jurisprudence the seller's duty of information with respect to the buyer. This duty will have to be assessed in light of the particular circumstances of the case. Then, should the seller consider that his products are potentially unsafe for consumers, owing to the high content of allergens, he should warn the buyer on the label or in the instructions of use.

In conclusion, under Belgian law there is no obligation to inform consumers of the allergen content of food. If the manufacturer chooses to do so, he must provide as accurate and complete information as possible. If that is not the case, the manufacturer will be liable for the damages caused.

Denmark

The Danish Acts relevant for this study are the following:

Product Liability Law (PLL) (1994-05-18N 364) (Implements EU Directive 92/59);
Law on Food Products (LFP) (1973-06-06 N 310 with amendments);
Law on Marketing (LM) (1994-06-01, N 428); and
Law on the Indemnity for Injuries and Loss of Breadwinner (LI) (51989-09-08 N 599 with amendments).

Apart from the general labelling obligations, under Danish law the manufacturer is not obliged specifically to inform consumers who suffer from intolerances to certain foodstuffs. The Product Liability Law (PLL) concerns only "dangerous products", but a product that is not "dangerous" to persons without allergic reactions does not become "dangerous" if it causes reactions to allergic persons. If the manufacturer chooses to inform consumers that his product is free from a particular ingredient, he must abide by the Law on Marketing (LM). This law requires that the information must "not be incorrect, misleading or unreasonably inadequate and may not affect the demand or offer of goods".

If a manufacturer chooses to inform consumers that his product is free from a particular ingredient, he is liable under PLL for injuries caused by his product if the information provided was incorrect.

France

According to French law, there is no obligation for manufacturers and sellers to indicate whether their products contain ingredients that could give rise to allergies as long as the product is not a new product (containing new ingredients resulting from research and development). This is not part of the general obligation that professional manufacturers and sellers have under French law to inform consumers of the essential characteristics of the product/service.

In fact, the allergic consumer is deemed to know the substance/ingredients to which he is allergic. Accordingly, he should acquaint himself with any possible risk before buying the product.

However, the Étude de I'Institut Français de la Nutrition has listed the six most common allergens that are likely to provoke the most serious reactions. In practice, manufacturers may mention those ingredients on the labels of their products to provide advance warning to the consumer. The listed products are groundnut, shrimps, milk, eggs, fish and soya.

If the manufacturer chooses to inform consumers, there is no specific requirement as to the rules/guidelines he should follow. However, labelling is the information process that is recommended by the Institut Français de la Nutrition.

The manufacturer incurs no liability for injuries that could be caused by allergic reactions to his product. This stems from the absence of any specific obligation to inform the consumer of the presence of allergens in his products.

Germany

According to German law, food manufacturers are not required to inform consumers who suffer from intolerance to certain foods of the presence or absence of potential allergens in the food. However, if the manufacturer chooses to inform consumers, he must provide information that is correct, complete, up-to-date and understandable. The manufacturer bears the risk for the accuracy of the information provided and will be liable for injuries or damage suffered by a consumer who relied on the information provided.

Greece

There is a variety of Greek health regulations that oblige manufacturers to provide information, through labelling, to consumers with specific health problems or that need special treatment (i.e. pregnant women, children, etc.). If the product is not intended for use by these consumers, it has only to meet the general European quality level, providing for safety requirements "under normal or reasonably foreseeable conditions of use".

Food manufacturers are not obliged to inform consumers about possible intolerance to certain food, but if the manufacturer chooses to do so he must follow these guidelines: if the information is accurate, consumers who know that they suffer from allergies consume the food at their own risk. However, not everyone who is an allergy sufferer is aware of their intolerance. Nevertheless, if the manufacturer has chosen to inform consumers of the possible risks, the consumer will find it difficult to prove that the food was "unsafe".

Portugal

According to Portuguese law, food manufacturers are not specifically required to inform consumers who suffer from intolerance to certain food products. The manufacturer only has the obligation to inform consumers about the compositions, ingredients, components and additives of the food before putting the products on the market as required by the law, and this information must be true and correct.

There are no rules or guidelines that the manufacturer has to follow if he chooses to inform consumers about possible intolerances to certain foodstuffs.

Information about food products must be true and correct. However, if the manufacturer decides to inform consumers suffering from food intolerances, he only will be held liable for the injuries caused by his products if he has presented incorrect information through negligence or if he has assumed liability for the damages caused by that information.

Spain

Spanish law on consumer protection provides every consumer with the right to obtain reliable and accurate information from every manufacturer. In relation to foodstuffs, the manufacturer of any type of food product is required to supply specific information related to the food produced, including the product's composition, ingredient, expiry date and weight. In addition to this general obligation, specific legislation regulates each foodstuff so that the manufacturer must also abide by the legislation governing the product at issue. Moreover, even if there is no contract between the consumer and the manufacturer, whenever injustices are caused by inaccurate information provided by the manufacturer, the manufacturer can be considered liable to that consumer, based upon negligent behaviour, if he had failed to take reasonable care in verifying the accuracy of the information. Therefore, even if the manufacturer has no legal obligation to provide such information, the giving of incorrect information could be considered a breach of care, resulting in damage to the consumer, especially in regard to the manufacturer's obligation to provide consumers with accurate information related to the product.

United Kingdom

Under UK law there is no absolute statutory obligation to inform consumers of food substances that might trigger allergies. However, that information often appears on the packaging of the food by reason of the various food labelling regulations. The provisions of these regulations impose, among others, the obligation for the manufacturer to use a specific and not a generic description of the product in the ingredients list; to mark on the label the category of additive used; and to apply specific provisions for certain food substances considered as allergens, such as nuts or figs. But there are still a lot of allergens that slip through this net of labelling requirements.

Under common law, it could be argued that the manufacturer has a duty to warn of a danger that is reasonably foreseeable, that is to say, a danger that is known or ought to have been known to involve a sufficiently serious risk. The degree of seriousness of the consequences may change the exact content of this duty. However, in order to determine the level of the manufacturer's duty of care, the provisions of the statutory régime must be examined. And, if the legislation does not provide that the manufacturer has to list allergens per se, then it will be very unlikely that such a duty of care will be imposed under common law.

Although there is no legal requirement to list allergens per se, as a matter of good practice the Ministry of Agriculture, Fisheries and Food (MAFF) has encouraged manufacturers to adhere to the following guidelines:

> Where a known allergen is used, the manufacturer should check whether the consumer would be alerted by the label, and, if not, to included a warning on the label.

> Where an allergen is used in replacement of a more general ingredient (for example vegetable oil is listed and groundnut oil used) the manufacturer should take the appropriate steps to make the presence of the allergen known down the food distribution chain.

MAFF has also encouraged the larger manufacturers to produce leaflets about the content of their food products so that the consumer is properly informed.

Under UK law, as we have seen above, there is no general statutory provision obliging manufacturers to include allergens on the label; however, they can do so voluntarily. English law provides for sanctions to manufacturers in the event that they provide incorrect information in any form whatsoever.

Thus, according to the Trade Description Act of 1968, if the manufacturer, or any other person who in the course of trade or business supplies or offers to supply goods, provides a "trade description" (which according to UK law includes information about the method of manufacture, production, processing, composition, etc.) that is false, the manufacturer may be liable to the criminal sanctions of a fine and/or a term of imprisonment.

The Consumer Protection Act of 1987 considers a product to be defective if it states in its label that it is free from an ingredient that triggers allergy, but in fact the product contain such ingredients. Thus, if the consumer suffers personal injury as a result of the defect in the product, the manufacturer will be held liable.

Under common law, if the information has been given negligently, then tortious liability will follow, and the manufacturer may be held liable for personal injury.

REFERENCES

1.   Treaty Establishing the European Economic Community, 25 March 1957, as amended, Article 36
      Office for Official Publications of the European Communities, Luxembourg.

2.   Council Directive on the approximation of the laws of the Member States relating to the labelling, presentation and advertising of foodstuffs for sale to the ultimate consumer, 79/112/EEC.
      Official Journal of the European Communities (1979) 22, L33, 8/3/79, 1-14

3.   Directive 97/4/EC of the European Parliament and of the Council amending Directive 79/112/EEC on the approximation of the laws of the Member States relating to the labelling, presentation and advertising of foodstuffs.
      Official Journal of the European Communities (1997) 40, L43, 14/2/97, 21-4

4.   Draft Proposal for a European Parliament and Council Directive amending Directive 79/112/EEC on the approximation of the laws of the Member States relating to the labelling, presentation and advertising of foodstuffs, III/5909/97, 27/1/97

5.   Draft Green Paper on General Principles of Food Law in the European Union, 30/8/96.

6. Commission Recommendation 97/77/EC concerning a co-ordinated programme for the official control of foodstuffs for 1997.
   Official Journal of the European Communities, 40, L22, 24/1/97, 27-34

7. Council Directive 89/397/EEC on the official control of foodstuffs.
   Official Journal of the European Communities, 32, L186, 30/6/89, 23-6

8. Commission Regulation (EC) No. 258/97 on novel foods and novel food ingredients.
   Official Journal of the European Communities, 40, L43, 14/2/97, 1-7

9. Proposed draft amendment to Codex General Standard for the labelling of prepackaged foods.
   Alinorm 97/22A, Appendix V.

10. UK Food Safety Act 1990
    London: HMSO Chapter 16

11. The Food Labelling Regulations 1996
    London: HMSO SI 1996 No. 1499

12. General Product Safety Regulations 1994
    London: HMSO SI 1994 No. 2328

13. Food Safety Code of Practice No. 16: Enforcement of the Food Safety Act 1990 in Relation to the Food Hazard Warning System.
    London: HMSO.

14. Ordinance on the Labelling and Presentation of Foodstuffs,
    Statens livsmedelsverks författningssamling SLV FS 1993 :19 (H130), 16/12/93, 1-28.

15. Guidelines on the Labelling of Foodstuffs, 1997
    Livsmedelsverket, 23.

16. Ordinance SLV FS 1995:15 (H130:2), 21/6/95, 1-2.

17. Order on the Labelling of Pre-packed Foods
    Finlands författningssamling (1991) 81, 15/5/91, 1562-70.

18. Notice to Manufacturers, Label Declaration of Allergenic Substances in Foods US Food and Drug Administration Centre for Food Safety and Applied Nutrition
    June 1996.

19. USFDA Code of Federal Regulations, Title 21, Part 105.62.

20.   Australian Food Standards Code, 1987, as amended.
       Australian Government Publishing Service.

21.   Canadian Food and Drug Regulations, B.24.019.

22.   Council Directive 89/398/EEC on the approximation of the laws of the
       Member States relating to foodstuffs intended for particular nutritional uses.
       Official Journal of the European Communities (1989) 32, L186, 27-32.

23.   Codex Standard for gluten-free foods, 118-1981.

24.   Order of 20 July 1977 on dietetic and dietary products.
       Journal Officiel de la République Française N.C. (138), 18/9/77, 5964-71.

25.   Public Health Regulations (Food) (Gluten Labelling) 5756-1996.

26.   Consumer and Corporate Affairs, Canada: Guide to Food Manufacturers
       and Advertisers.

27.   Article 173, Swiss Food Code.

28.   Commission Directive 96/5/EC on processed cereal-based foods and baby
       foods for infants and young children.
       Official Journal of the European Communities (1996) 39, L49, 17-28

29.   Commission Directive 91/321/EEC on infant formulae and follow-on
       formulae.
       Official Journal of the European Communities (1991) 34, L175, 35-49.